Laboratory Activities Manual
Teacher Edition

D1471575

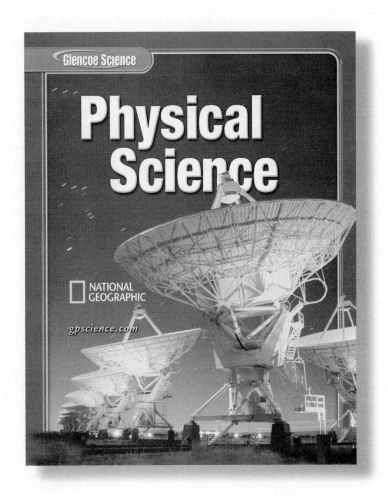

Glencoe Science

Physical Science

NATIONAL GEOGRAPHIC

gpscience.com

 **Glencoe**

New York, New York   Columbus, Ohio   Chicago, Illinois   Peoria, Illinois   Woodland Hills, California

To the Teacher

Activities in *Glencoe Physical Science Laboratory Activities Manual* do not require elaborate supplies or extensive pre-lab preparations. They are designed to explore science through a stimulating yet simple and relaxed approach to each topic. Helpful comments, suggestions, and answers to all questions are provided at the back of the *Teacher Edition.*

Activities in this laboratory manual are student-oriented. The scientific conclusions desired are not valid for any student unless he or she is directly involved in obtaining them. The activities should be performed by students only with your supervision. Directions are straightforward, so students can follow them easily. Students should be able to work through a problem to a satisfactory answer. The design of the manual is such that students should be interested enough to do their own investigating and not accept conclusions made by someone else. Students should discover their own mistakes through a review of the introductory statement, **Strategy**, and **Procedure**. If students still cannot reach a satisfactory conclusion, assistance in interpreting data may be needed.

Each activity can be torn from the book and handed in when the lab has been completed. Although the labs are not designed as a grading device, they can serve as a measure of progress for you and your students.

Most labs can be completed in a single class period. Some do not require the entire period; others require portions of two or more consecutive periods. Some require a preliminary setup followed by several inspections.

Glencoe

The *McGraw·Hill* Companies

Send all inquiries to:
Glencoe/McGraw-Hill
8787 Orion Place
Columbus, OH 43240

ISBN 0-07-866085-8
Printed in the United States of America
1 2 3 4 5 6 7 8 9 10   045   09 08 07 06 05 04

Table of Contents

Inquiry in the Science Laboratory

What is inquiry?

The process of inquiry models actual science practice, encourages problem-solving strategies, and develops critical-thinking skills. Students are actively involved in the learning process when they determine materials, procedures, and the topics and questions they want to investigate.

Inquiry can range from a very structured activity for those students who need more guidance, to a more open-ended approach in which students design their investigations. We encourage you to modify the labs in this manual in a manner that best supports your students.

Why is inquiry important?

Inquiry activities, such as those in *Glencoe's Laboratory Activities Manual*, will help students develop educational, career, and life skills. Students learn how to think for themselves, how to solve problems, and how to apply prior knowledge to new situations.

How can this book help?

Glencoe's Laboratory Activities Manual is structured to give support to both teachers and students. Important scientific concepts are the core of each lab. Students gain practice in developing and testing their own hypotheses, designing experiments, gathering and analyzing data, and communicating their conclusions to their peers. Teachers are given strategies to guide students who need additional structure and to encourage students who are ready for more open-ended exploration.

Suggestions for Incorporating Inquiry in the Science Classroom

Inquiry in science does take extra time, just as it would in a research lab. Here are some ways you might be able to efficiently incorporate inquiry into your classroom.

- Supply various materials that are related to the concept you are trying to convey and allow students to explore them in groups for about 15 minutes. Have groups brainstorm ideas and list questions they have about those concepts. Have them list materials they will need. As a class or on your own, eliminate those questions that cannot be answered in the classroom. Gather any additional materials that are needed and allow students to begin their explorations the next day or the next week.

- Have students brainstorm questions they would like to explore. As a class, choose 1 or 2 reasonable questions that each group will explore in its own way. (This is very helpful if you are trying to cover a specific topic.)

Inquiry in the Science Laboratory (continued)

- Give your students a more guided activity that relates hard-to-understand concepts and skills. Then, allow them to explore on their own with a wider variety of materials. Make sure you allow time for debriefing so the students (and you) will understand what they learned from the experience.

- Students will need practice doing inquiry before they should be allowed to explore completely on their own. Be sure to give them lots of practice in using the tools of science so that their explorations are more successful.

- Encourage students to rely on their data and not on what they think the answer should be. If their data are unexpected, help them to problem-solve what might have happened.

Developing Process Skills

Basic Process Skills

Observe: Students use one or more senses to learn more about objects and events.

Classify: Students group objects or events based on common properties and/or categorize based on existing relationships among objects or events.

Infer: Students propose interpretations, explanations, and causes from observed events and collected data.

Communicate: Students convey information verbally, both in oral and written forms, and visually through graphs, charts, pictures, and diagrams.

Measure in SI: Students identify length, area, volume, mass, and temperature to describe and quantify objects or events.

Predict: Students propose possible results or outcomes of future events based on observations and inferences drawn from previous events.

Calculate: Students transfer or apply ordering, counting, adding, subtracting, multiplying, and dividing to quantify data where appropriate.

Complex Process Skills

Interpret Data: Students explain the meaning of information gathered in scientific situations.

Form Hypotheses: Students make an informed assumption in order to draw out and test its logical consequences.

Experiment: Students test hypotheses or predictions under conditions in which variables are both controlled and manipulated.

Formulate Models: Students construct mental, verbal, or physical representations of ideas, objects, or events. The models are then used to clarify explanations or to demonstrate relationships.

Analyze Results: Students evaluate the outcome of an experiment to determine if it is reasonable. They should be able to draw conclusions and make inferences from the results.

Introducing/Reviewing Laboratory Work

Following proper techniques when using laboratory equipment helps prevent accidents and cuts down on the cost of replacement materials and devices. Students' success also is increased as their familiarity with the devices and their measurement and analysis skills increase. To facilitate student success in the classroom laboratory, first familiarize yourself with the general organization of Glencoe's science activities. The organization varies according to the type of activity. Then orient the students to the laboratory setting. This includes reviewing equipment and correct handling procedures with them, the use of SI units in their activities, and assessing their readiness for work in the laboratory.

Organization of Glencoe Science Laboratory Activities

- An **introductory statement** explains the science concepts involved in the activity. Specific information for the investigation of the problem is re-emphasized. This statement appears under the investigation title.

- A **strategy** or **list of objectives** provide objectives for student performance. If the student does not understand the goal(s) of the activity, a rereading of the section is advised.

- **Materials** is the list of all materials or possible materials needed for the activity. The **Materials** section should be previewed so that any supplies to be contributed by students may be obtained in advance. Be sure to assemble these materials *before* the beginning of a class period.

- A **safety precautions** section provides **icons** to prompt safety awareness and general **warning statement(s)** pertinent to the activity.

- Some labs include a section that states the **problem** or **what will be investigated**.

- Some labs have students state a **hypothesis**.

- **Procedure** is the step-by-step set of instructions for the activity. You may want to discuss the procedure with students before they begin the activity. Pre-activity discussions help prevent misuse of equipment and injuries that can result from careless use of the glassware, burners, and/or corrosive chemicals. Specific **safety warning statements** are placed appropriately in the **Procedure** section.

- **Data and Observations** includes sample graphs, charts, and tables to help improve students' analysis skills. Emphasis should be placed on the need to record all observations during and at the completion of the activity. In many cases, recorded data provide the necessary link in cause-and-effect relationships. Each student should do his or her own computations except in those activities where group work or class averages are required.

- An **analysis** or **questions and conclusions** section contains discussion questions and blanks for student answers at the end of each activity. These questions are designed to review main ideas, to direct attention to key parts of the procedure, and to relate the material to science concepts and applications. Answering these questions promotes and reinforces student learning.

- A **strategy check** or **hypothesis check** section allows students to evaluate the activity. If a student can place a checkmark in the blank provided, he or she has gained a skill, interpreted a concept, or learned a process.

Evaluating Activity Work

Evaluation of the activities and of the general outcomes of laboratory work is a difficult task. Pure recognition and recall tests are not usually suitable for evaluating laboratory experience. Evaluation methods that depend on accurate observation, recognition of pertinent data, and ability to reason logically are more suitable for measuring outcomes of laboratory work. This type of evaluation may be done through periodic checking of student notebooks or individual or group conferences. You may also require students to submit laboratory reports. Laboratory reports should include

- a clearly stated problem.
- a procedure outlined in detail.
- data organized in good form and understandable; may include
    - **a.** labeled diagrams.
    - **b.** labeled and titled graphs.
    - **c.** data tables.
- conclusions that answer the problem based on data obtained in the activity.
- a report that is clear enough to serve as a future review of the material.

The following questions should be answered in evaluating an activity report.

- Is the report written clearly enough so that an uninformed person could read it and know exactly what was being attempted, how it was done, and what conclusions were reached?
- Can the student duplicate the experiment using the report alone as a guide?

Achievement tests designed to assess understanding of course content are an important evaluation technique for laboratory work. Knowledge should be obtained through correct laboratory methods.

- You may wish to observe techniques used, correctness of procedures, and results obtained. An observational checklist based on objectives could be used.
- You may wish to direct students to perform a laboratory task in a practical test. Students should be able to satisfactorily complete this test before beginning laboratory work. For this test, set up equipment stations in the classroom. At each station, provide instructions.

Station 1: **Lighting a Laboratory Burner**
Equipment: laboratory burner, rubber hose, gas outlet, gas lighter or safety matches
Instructions: Correctly set up and light the burner and adjust the flame.

Station 2: **Decanting and Filtering**
Equipment: two beakers—one containing a mixture of water and sand; stirring rod; filter paper; funnel; ring stand
Instructions: Decant the clear liquid from the residue. Correctly set up the equipment for a filtration procedure.

Station 3: **Using the Balance**
Equipment: balance, rubber stopper
Instructions: Correctly carry the balance from Station 3 to your desk and back to Station 3. Determine the mass of the rubber stopper.

Evaluating Activity Work (continued)

Station 4: **Measuring Temperature**
Equipment: thermometer, beaker of water
Instructions: Position the thermometer correctly and determine the temperature of the water in the beaker.

Station 5: **Measuring Volume**
Equipment: graduated cylinder containing colored water
Instructions: Determine the volume of water in the graduated cylinder.

Station 6: **Identifying Parts of a Microscope**
Equipment: microscope, labels
Instructions: Correctly identify the labeled parts of this microscope.

Station 7: **Using a Microscope**
Equipment: microscope, prepared slide
Instructions: Correctly carry the microscope from Station 7 to your desk and back to Station 7. Place the slide on the stage and bring the slide into sharp focus.

Station 8: **Inserting Glass Tubing into a Rubber Stopper**
Equipment: glass tubing, glycerol or soapy water, one-hole rubber stopper, cloth towel
Instructions: Insert the glass tubing into the rubber stopper.

Introducing/Reviewing Laboratory Safety Guidelines

Safe Laboratory Conduct

Whether you are a first-time or very experienced teacher, a review of safety guidelines is in order. This section deals with behaviors and actions that foster a safe learning environment. Because you serve as the role model for the behavior in the laboratory that you expect from your students, first review the safety guidelines for teachers. Then, on the first day of classes, introduce or review the safety guidelines that are the students' responsibility.

Teacher Safety Guidelines

- Thoroughly review your local safety regulations and this manual. Modify any activities to comply with your local regulations. For example, open flames are NOT permitted in some states or communities.

- Be trained in first aid and CPR.

- Be aware of students with allergies or other medical conditions that might limit their activities or require special protective equipment, such as facemasks.

- Have a list of substances to be used in lab activities made available to the doctor of any pregnant teacher or student so that limitations may be determined beforehand.

- NEVER leave students unattended in the classroom or field setting.

- NEVER be alone or out of earshot of someone when you prepare lab activities or equipment.

- Always wash your hands with antibacterial soap and warm water upon entering the laboratory, after live cultures have been handled, after cleanup, and before removing safety goggles.

- NEVER perform an investigation on any animal that might be a health hazard to humans or cause pain or suffering to the animal.

- Use protista and other invertebrates for lab or field activities involving animals when possible. Protista represent a wide variety of organisms and can be obtained in large quantities.

- A qualified adult supervisor who has had training in the proper care and handling of laboratory animals must assume responsibility for the conditions of any activity that involves living vertebrates. NO activity/investigation should be conducted that involves drugs, organisms pathogenic to humans or other vertebrates, ionizing radiation, surgical procedures, or carcinogens unless the procedures have been approved by and will be performed or supervised by a qualified biomedical scientist.

Introducing/Reviewing
Laboratory Safety Guidelines (continued)

- Have students notify you beforehand if they plan to bring in a pet for observation.

- Instruct students about the hazards involved with wild animals and your school's policy and local and state laws regarding their capture and use in the classroom/laboratory. **WARNING:** *Wild animals may exhibit unpredictable behaviors, may become dangerous as they mature, and if declawed, may not be accepted by zoos and will probably die if released into the wild.* **WARNING:** *There is the potential of contracting rabies from any infected warm-blooded animal.*

- It is recomended that you purchase fumigated, steam sterilized materials. **WARNING:**

  - *Owl pellets can be a source of salmonella.*

  - *Bird nests contain many organisms that can cause diseases.*

  - *Bird eggs, even if disinfected when first acquired, will decay after a few days from gases building up in them. Rotten eggs produce noxious odors.*

  - *Some insects carry diseases that are serious if transmitted to humans.*

Presenting Safety Guidelines to Students

- Review the use and location of safety equipment, evacuation guidelines, and first aid procedures. Refer to fire drill regulations and a chart of emergency procedures, which should be posted in a prominent place in the laboratory. Assign safety partners and explain their role in helping during emergencies.

- Discuss safe disposal of materials and laboratory cleanup policy.

- Preview Glencoe's science activities with students and discuss the safety icons and their meanings (see p. 17). Point out the warning statements and the importance of heeding them. Distribute the Safety Symbols reference sheet (see p. 14).

- Distribute and discuss Student Laboratory and Safety Guidelines (see p. 15). Emphasize proper attitudes for working in the laboratory and field and review or present school rules regarding the consequences of misbehavior. Stress the need for safe practices on the part of everyone involved. Then distribute the Student Science Laboratory Safety Contract found on p. 16. You may wish to have each student and parent or guardian sign a safety contract at the beginning of each course. Review the safety guidelines and safety contract with students at least once a month.

Preparation of Solutions

It is most important to use safe laboratory techniques when handling all chemicals. Many substances may appear harmless but are, in fact, toxic, corrosive, or very reactive. Always check with the supplier. Chemicals should never be ingested. Be sure to use proper techniques to smell solutions or other agents. Always wear safety goggles, gloves, and an apron. Observe the following precautions.

1. *Poisonous/corrosive liquid and/or vapor*—use in the fume hood; Examples: acetic acid, nitric acid, hydrochloric acid, ammonium hydroxide
2. *Poisonous and corrosive to eyes, lungs, and skin;* Examples: acids, limewater, iron(III) chloride, bases, silver nitrate, iodine, potassium permanganate
3. *Poisonous if swallowed, inhaled, or absorbed through the skin;* Examples: glacial acetic acid, copper compounds, barium chloride, lead compounds, chromium compounds, lithium compounds, cobalt(II) chloride, silver compounds
4. Always add acids to water, never the reverse.
5. When sulfuric acid and sodium hydroxide are added to water, a large amount of thermal energy is released. Sodium metal reacts violently with water. Use extra care when handling any of these substances.

Aluminum nitrate solution: Dissolve 5.3 g in 250 mL water

Ascorbic acid (vitamin C solution): Dissolve 250 mg in 250 mL water

Benedict's solution (sugar indicator): Dissolve 100 g of anhydrous sodium carbonate and 173 g sodium citrate in 700 mL of distilled water. Heat the water until the salts are dissolved. Dissolve 17.3 g copper sulfate in 100 mL of water. Pour it slowly into the solution, stirring constantly. Allow the mixture to cool and then add enough distilled water to make 1 L.

Cobalt nitrate solution: Dissolve 4.6 g in 250 mL water

Copper (II) nitrate solution: Dissolve 4.7 g in 250 mL water

Copper (II) sulfate solution: Dissolve 6.3 g copper (II) sulfate pentahydrate salt in 250 mL water

Glucose solution: Dissolve 4.5 anhydrous glucose (dextrose) in 250 mL water

Glycerol solution: Dissolve 5 mL glycerin (glycerol) in 250 mL water

Hydrochloric acid (HCl): Stir 82 mL of concentrated (12 M) HCl into 1 L water to make 1.0 M solution

Hydrochloric acid (HCl) dilute, aq: Add 25 mL of 1.0 M solution above to 225 mL of water

Indophenol testing reagent (vitamin C indicator): Dissolve 250 mg of sodium salt of indophenol powder in 250 mL water

Iodine solution: Add 25 mL Lugol's solution to 225 mL water

Iron (II) nitrate solution: Dissolve 4.5 g in 250 mL water

Iron (III) nitrate solution: Dissolve 6.0 g in 250 mL water

Lugol's solution (starch indicator): Dissolve 25 g potassium iodide in 250 mL water. Add 12.5 g iodine crystals. Stir thoroughly. Store in dark bottle away from strong light to keep indefinitely.

Magnesium nitrate solution: Dissolve 3.7 g in 250 mL water

Preparation of Solutions (continued)

Methylene blue solution: Dissolve 0.3 g methylene blue powder in 30 mL 95% ethanol. Add 100 mL distilled water.

Nickel nitrate solution: Dissolve 4.5 g in 250 mL water

Silver nitrate solution: Dissolve 2.1 g in 250 mL water

Sodium carbonate solution: Dissolve 26.3 g in 250 mL water

Sodium chloride solution: Dissolve 14.6 g in 250 mL water

Sodium hydroxide solution: Dissolve 5 g in 250 mL water

Sodium iodide solution: Dissolve 3.7 g in 250 mL water

Sulfuric acid solution: Add 14 mL of concentrated (18 M) acid to 250 mL water

Universal indicator solution: Add the following to 250 mL water:
38 mg phenolphthalein (disodium salt)
38 mg bromthymol blue (sodium salt)
28 mg methyl orange (sodium salt)
56 mg alizarine yellow R(sodium salt)
19 mg bromcresol green(sodium salt)
38 mg meta cresol purple
Note: This will store indefinitely in a sealed plastic bottle.

Zinc nitrate solution: Dissolve 4.7 g in 250 mL water

Lab Preparation

Laboratory Equipment and Supplies

This table of equipment and inexpensive, easily accessible materials can help you prepare for your science class. The quantities listed are for one class of 30 students working in pairs. Some experiments may require larger groups of students due to equipment and space limitations.

It is assumed that goggles, laboratory aprons, gloves, tap water, textbooks, paper, calculators, pencils, and pens are available for all activities

Non-Consumables	
Item	**Experiments used in**
Alligator clips	7-1, 20-2
Ammeter	9-1
Audio amplifier, mini	12-2
Baking tray, large	18-2
Battery clip, 9-V, mini	7-2, 20-2
Battery, 1.5 V, dry cell	8-2, 15-2
Battery, 9-V, dry cell	7-2, 20-2
BBs, iron	8-2
Beaker, 100 mL	24-1
Beaker, 250 mL	6-1, 7-1, 16-2, 18-2, 24-1
Beaker, 500 mL	22-1
Beakers, same size	11-2, 21-2
Books	1-1, 3-2, 4-2, 14-1, 14-2, 16-2
Bowl	13-1
Bowling ball	2-2
Buckets	10-1
Calculator	12-1, 12-2
Candles	12-2
Car (toy)	4-2
Carpeting, rough strip	4-2
Ceramic tile	25-1
Clothespins, spring-loaded	10-1
Coins, all of same type	1-2
Comb	14-1
Computer	12-2
Convex lens, thick	14-2
Convex lens, thin	14-2
Copper wire, insulated	15-2, 20-2, 25-1
Dowel, 3/4 in.	10-2

Lab Preparation (continued)

Non-Consumables	
Item	**Experiments used in**
Dropper	10-2, 15-2
Flashlight	12-1, 14-1
Flask, 100 mL	6-2
Forceps	19-1, 23-2
Glass plate	10-2
Glass rods	7-1, 22-1
Graduated cylinder, 10 mL	22-2
Graduated cylinder, 100 mL	6-2, 7-1, 9-2, 22-1
Hammer	11-2
Hand lens *or* magnifier	17-1
Hot plate, laboratory burner, *or* immersion heater	16-2, 21-2, 22-2
Iron bolts	8-2
Iron filings	8-1
Iron *or* lead washer	16-2
Lamp	15-2
Lamp socket	13-2
Light emitting diodes (LEDs)	7-2, 12-2, 20-2
Light socket and cord	9-1
Lightbulbs: 25, 60, 75, 100 W	9-1, 13-2
Magnet, horseshoe, small	8-1
Magnets, bar	8-1, 12-2, 15-2
Mass set	1-1, 3-2, 5-2
Meterstick	2-1, 3-2, 4-2, 5-1, 5-2, 9-1, 10-1, 11-2, 12-1, 13-2
Metric balance	1-2, 3-2, 6-1, 6-2, 16-1, 21-1, 22-2
Metric ruler	1-1, 1-2, 4-1, 7-2, 9-2, 12-1, 14-2, 15-1, 16-2, 19-1, 19-2
Metric spring scale	2-1, 5-1, 5-2
Microplate, 24 well	15-1, 16-2, 19-1, 19-2, 20-2
Microplate, 96 well	17-1, 20-1, 23-1, 23-2, 24-2
Mirror, plane	14-1
Momentum cart	3-2
Multimeter *or* ohmeter	13-2
Nails, various lengths	7-1, 11-2, 21-2
Pan, aluminum	6-2

Lab Preparation (continued)

Non-Consumables	
Item	**Experiments used in**
Paper clips	6-2
Paper punch, one hole	6-1
Paraffin block	10-2
Pennies	17-2
Photo resistor	13-2
Pillow, large	2-2
Pillowcase	4-2
Pipettes	6-1, 15-1, 16-1, 16-2, 17-1, 19-1, 19-2, 20-1, 20-2, 21-1, 23-1, 23-2, 24-2
Plastic container with shaker top	8-1
Pliers	16-2
Pot holder	22-2
Prism	12-1, 13-1
Projector *or* other light source	12-2, 13-1, 14-1
Protractor	14-1
Pulleys	3-2, 5-2
Radio	12-2
Resistor switch	9-1
Resistor, 1000 Ω	20-2
Resistor, 500 Ω	7-2
Ring	4-1
Ring clamp	1-1
Ring stand	1-1, 3-2, 4-1, 5-2, 6-2, 9-1, 13-2
Ripple bar	10-2
Ripple tank, light source, bottom screen	10-2
Roller skates	2-1
Rope *or* coiled spring toy	10-1
Rubber stoppers	10-2, 24-1
Sandpaper, coarse	4-2
Scissors	7-2, 9-2, 11-2, 12-1, 13-1, 15-1, 19-1,19-2, 23-2
Sinkers	4-1
Skating safety equipment (helmet, pads)	2-1
Solar cell	9-1
Soldering tool	25-1
Spoon, metal	11-2, 21-2
Spoon, wooden	11-2

Lab Preparation (continued)

Non-Consumables

Item	Experiments used in
Stapler and staples	7-2
Stopwatches	2-1, 2-2, 3-1, 3-2, 17-2, 21-2, 22-1, 23-2
Telephone pickup coil	12-2
Test-tube holder	6-1, 21-2, 22-2, 24-1
Test tubes	6-1, 15-2, 21-2, 22-2, 24-1
Test-tube rack	6-1, 15-2, 22-2, 24-1
Thermometer	6-1, 6-2, 9-2, 22-2, 24-1
Tongs	21-2
Tubing, rubber or plastic	9-2
Utility clamp	3-2, 5-2, 6-2, 9-1, 13-2
Vacuum cleaner	12-2
Voltmeter	7-1, 9-1
Watch	4-1, 6-2, 12-2, 24-1
Water rocket and launcher (toy)	3-1
Wire	7-1
Wire cutters	11-2
Wire ties, plastic-coated	1-1, 3-2, 5-2, 7-1
Wire, insulated	8-2, 9-1
Wood block, 1 cm x 1 cm x 15 cm	11-2
Wood block, 15 cm x 10 cm x 5 cm	11-2
Wooden dowel rods	5-1

Consumables

Item	Experiments used in
Aluminum foil	7-2, 21-2, 21-2, 25-1
Aluminum pie pans, small	22-2
Aluminum strips	17-1
Black cloth or paper	9-2
Bleach, household	11-2
Bowls, plastic	11-2
Boxes or containers for planting	18-1
Camera, instant-developing	10-1
Cardboard	7-2, 8-1, 20-2
Cardboard boxes	9-2, 11-1
Cardboard tubes	11-2
Caulking	25-2
Chalk	15-2
Coat hangers, wire	11-2

Lab Preparation (continued)

Consumables	
Item	**Experiments used in**
Coin rolls, paper	1-2
Copper strips	15-2, 17-1
Epoxy cement	25-2
Filter paper	15-1
Food-almonds	6-2
Food-baking soda	21-2
Food-corn oil	16-1
Food-corn syrup	16-1
Food-dried lima beans	18-2
Food-dried split peas	11-2, 18-2
Food-lemon juice	23-1
Food-milk	23-1
Food-orange drink	24-2
Food-orange juice, bottled	24-2
Food-orange juice, freshly squeezed	24-2
Food-peanuts	6-2
Food-salt	22-1
Food-soda water, bottle, unopened	22-2
Food-toast	15-2
Food-uncooked rice	11-2
Food-walnuts	6-2
Graph paper	9-2
Index cards	13-1, 14-2
Iron strips	15-2, 17-1
Kitchen matches	15-2
Liquid soap	23-1
Magnesium strips	17-1
Marble chips	19-1
Margarine tubs, empty	11-2, 25-2
Marker, black, felt tip	3-2, 12-1
Marking pens: red, green, black	8-2, 15-1
Matches	6-2, 19-1, 19-2, 21-2
Nail polish, clear	13-1
Newspaper	25-2
Nickel strips	17-1

Lab Preparation (continued)

Consumables

Item	Experiments used in
Paper cups	25-2
Paper towel	6-1, 7-1, 15-1, 17-1, 21-1, 21-2, 22-1, 23-2
Paper, white	12-1, 13-1, 14-1, 17-1, 20-1, 23-1, 23-2, 24-2
Paper: red, orange, yellow, green, blue, violet, black	12-1
Pencils *or* pens	14-1, 15-1
Pencils, colored	13-2, 17-2
Pencils, unsharpened	13-2
Plastic bag, resealable	15-1, 21-1, 23-2, 25-2
Plastic container, lid	17-2, 25-2
Plastic cups	8-2, 16-1, 16-2, 20-1, 22-1, 25-2
Plastic cups with lids	6-1
Plastic foam cup	9-2
Plastic foam sheet	3-2
Plastic soda bottles, lids	11-2, 25-2
Plastic, clear	8-1
Potting soil	18-1
Putty	25-2
Rock salt	22-2
Rubber bands	3-2, 11-2
Rubber bands, equal lengths, different widths	1-1, 11-1
Rubber cement	25-2
Rubber sample	15-2
Seeds	18-1
Seeds, irradiated	18-1
Shoe box *or* tissue box	11-2
Solder wire, tin	25-1
Staples, wire	11-2
Steel wool	21-2
Straws	23-2
String	3-2, 4-1, 5-1, 11-2, 12-2, 21-2
String, cotton	5-2
Superglue	25-2
Tape, black	13-2
Tape, cellophane	12-1

Lab Preparation (continued)

Consumables

Item	Experiments used in
Tape, masking	2-1, 3-2, 4-2, 5-2, 8-1, 8-2, 9-1, 13-1, 13-2, 14-1, 14-2, 15-1, 15-2, 16-2, 20-2
Tape, transparent	7-2, 9-2, 11-2, 19-1
Tin strips	7-1
Toothpicks	19-1, 19-2, 25-2
Trash bag, plastic	11-2
Water	3-1, 6-1, 6-2, 9-2, 11-2, 13-1, 16-2, 22-1, 22-2
Water, distilled	15-1, 16-1, 17-1, 19-1, 19-2, 20-1, 20-2, 22-2, 23-1, 23-2, 24-2
Water, lime	19-1
Wax paper	25-2
Wood sample	15-2
Wood splint	6-2
Yarn, colored	10-1
Zinc strips	7-1, 17-1

Solutions

Chemical	Experiments used in
Aluminum nitrate solution	17-1
Ascorbic acid (Vitamin C solution)	24-2
Benedict's solution (sugar indicator)	24-1
Calcium carbonate	23-2
Cobalt nitrate solution	19-2
Copper (II) nitrate solution	17-1
Copper (II) sulfate solution	21-2
Diastase solution (saliva substitute)	24-1
Ethanol	15-1, 16-1
Glucose solution	20-2
Glycerol solution	20-2
Hydrochloric acid (HCl)	7-1, 15-2, 21-1
Hydrochloric acid (HCl) dilute	20-1
Hydrochloric acid (HCl) solution	19-1, 23-1, 23-2
Indophenol testing reagent (Vitamin C indicator)	24-2
Iodine solution	15-2
Iron (II) nitrate solution	17-1

Lab Preparation (continued)

Solutions	
Chemical	**Experiments used in**
Iron (III) nitrate solution	20-1
Lugol's solution (starch indicator)	24-1
Magnesium nitrate solution	17-1
Methylene blue solution	16-2
Nickel nitrate solution	17-1
Potassium bromide	22-2
Silver nitrate solution	20-1, 20-2
Sodium carbonate solution	20-1
Sodium chloride	22-2
Sodium chloride solution	20-2
Sodium hydrogen carbonate	21-1
Sodium hydroxide solution	20-2, 23-1
Sodium iodide solution	20-1
Sulfuric acid solution	20-2
Universal indicator solution	23-1, 23-2
Zinc nitrate solution	17-1

Answers to Student Laboratory Equipment Worksheets

Laboratory Equipment

Figure 1

1. Graduated cylinders **2.** Florence flask **3.** Beakers **4.** Crucible **5.** Petri dish
6. Evaporating dish **7.** Erlenmeyer flask **8.** Long-stem funnel **9.** Watch glass

Figure 2

1. Test tubes **2.** Test-tube rack **3.** Square-bottomed test tubes **4.** Rubber stoppers
5. Corks **6.** Test-tube holder **7.** Test-tube brush

Figure 3

1. Utility clamp **2.** Wire gauze **3.** Metal ring **4.** Laboratory burner **5.** Gas inlet
6. Ring stand

Figure 4

1. Stirring rod **2.** Funnel

Figure 5

1. Thermometer **2.** Pipette **3.** Rubber tubing **4.** Pinch clamp **5.** Dropper **6.** Spatula
7. Stirring rod **8.** Triangular file **9.** Forceps **10.** Scalpel

Figure 6

1. Eyepiece **2.** Revolving nosepiece **3.** High-power objective lens **4.** Low-power
objective lens **5.** Stage **6.** Diaphragm **7.** Adjustment knob **8.** Light

Figure 7

1. Hickman still head **2.** Conical reaction vials **3.** Air reflux condenser **4.** Claisen head
5. Hirsch funnel **6.** Filter flask **7.** Erlenmeyer flask (10 mL) **8.** Funnel **9.** Reaction tubes
10. Magnetic stir bars **11.** Connector with support rod **12.** Pipette **13.** Stopper
14. Spatula **15.** Centrifuge tube **16.** Glass tube connectors **17.** Syringe **18.** Flasks
19. Tubing **20.** One-way stopcock **21.** Connectors **22.** Thermometer connectors

Figure 8

1. Berol pipettes **2.** Blue litmus vial and litmus discs **3.** Microstand **4.** Plastic tubing
(long and short) **5.** Zinc electrode **6.** Zinc coil **7.** Iron electrode **8.** Various tubes
9. Microspatulas **10.** Dual well comboplate **11.** Microburner **12.** Syringe
13. Chromatography paper strips **14.** pH color chart **15.** Gas collecting vial
16. Microcaps **17.** Compass **18.** Microlids **19.** Current LED indicator

Getting Started

Science is the body of information including all the hypotheses and experiments that tell us about our environment. All people involved in scientific work use similar methods for gaining information. One important scientific skill is the ability to obtain data directly from the environment. Observations must be based on what actually happens in the environment. Equally important is the ability to organize these data into a form from which valid conclusions can be drawn. These conclusions must be such that other scientists can achieve the same results in the laboratory.

To make the most of your laboratory experience, you need to continually work to increase your laboratory skills. These skills include the ability to recognize and use equipment properly and to measure and use SI units accurately. Safety also must be an ongoing concern. To help you get started in discovering many fascinating things about the world around you, the next few pages provide you with:

- a visual overview of basic **laboratory equipment** for you to label
- a reference sheet of **SI units**
- a reference sheet of **safety symbols**
- a list of your **safety responsibilities** in the laboratory
- a **safety contract**

Each lab activity in this manual includes the following sections:
- an investigation **title** and introductory section providing information about the problem under study
- a **strategy** section identifying the **objective(s)** of the activity
- a list of needed **materials**
- safety concerns identified with **safety icons** and **caution statements**
- a set of step-by-step **procedures**
- a section to help you record your **data and observations**
- a section to help you **analyze your data** and record your **conclusions**
- a closing **strategy check** so that you can review your achievement of the objectives of the activity

Laboratory Equipment

Figure 1

1. _____

2. _____

3. _____

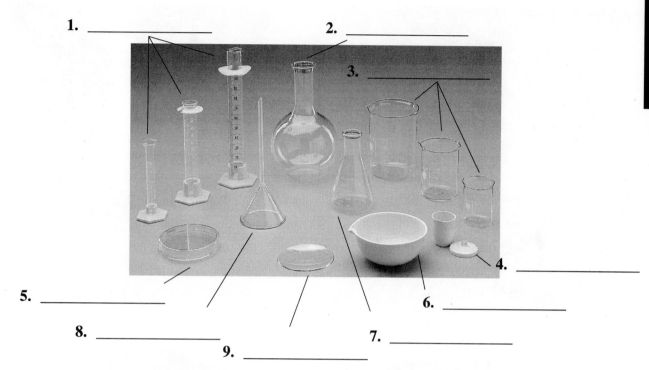

4. _____

5. _____

6. _____

7. _____

8. _____

9. _____

Figure 2

1. _____

2. _____

3. _____

4. _____

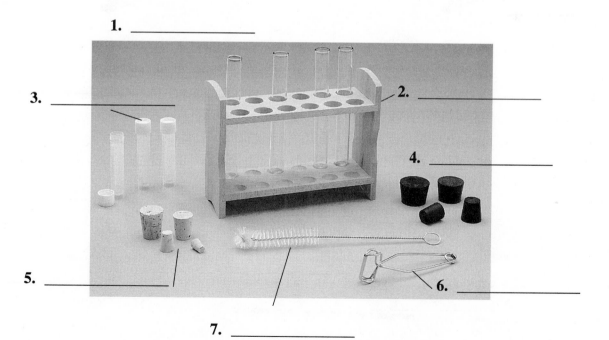

5. _____

6. _____

7. _____

Laboratory Equipment (continued)

Figure 3

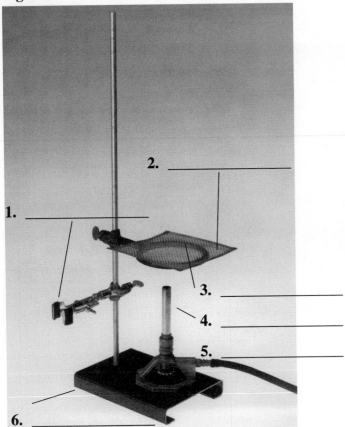

1. _____
2. _____
3. _____
4. _____
5. _____
6. _____

Figure 4

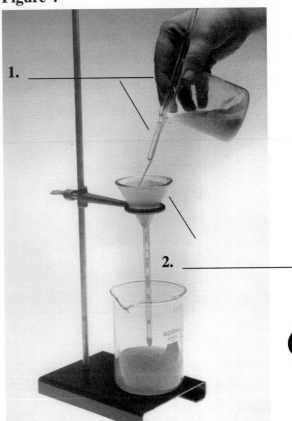

1. _____
2. _____

Figure 5

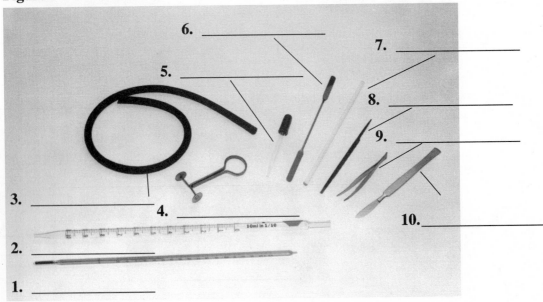

1. _____
2. _____
3. _____
4. _____
5. _____
6. _____
7. _____
8. _____
9. _____
10. _____

Laboratory Equipment (continued)

Getting Started

Figure 6

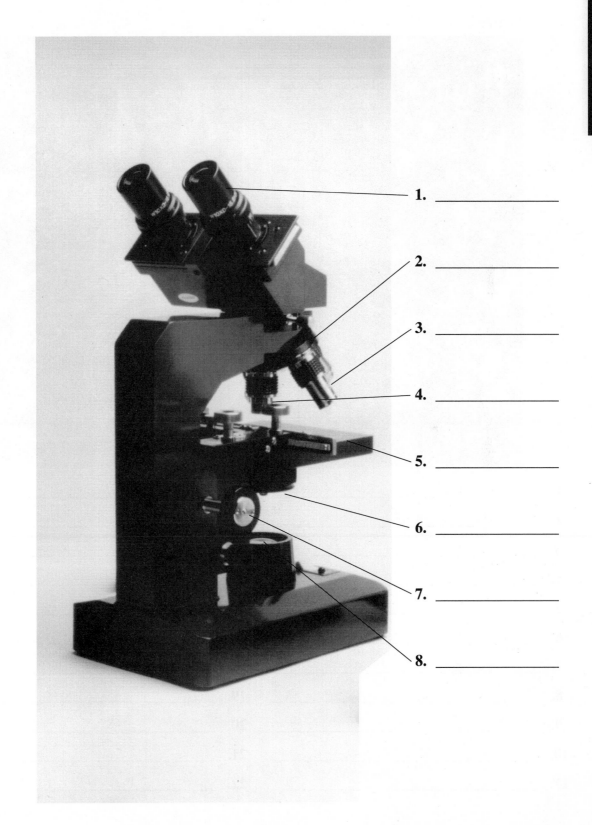

1. _____

2. _____

3. _____

4. _____

5. _____

6. _____

7. _____

8. _____

Getting Started

Laboratory Equipment (continued)

Figure 7

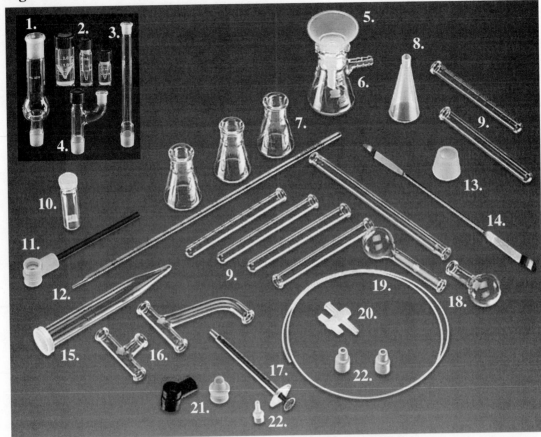

1. _____
2. _____
3. _____
4. _____
5. _____
6. _____
7. _____
8. _____
9. _____
10. _____
11. _____

12. _____
13. _____
14. _____
15. _____
16. _____
17. _____
18. _____
19. _____
20. _____
21. _____
22. _____

Laboratory Equipment (continued)

Figure 8

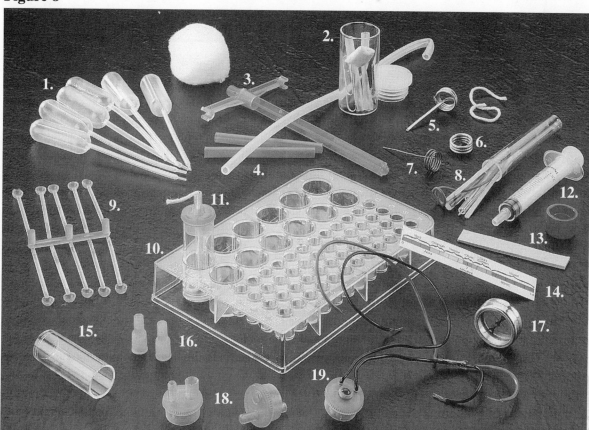

1. _____   11. _____
2. _____   12. _____
3. _____   13. _____
4. _____   14. _____
5. _____   15. _____
6. _____   16. _____
7. _____   17. _____
8. _____   18. _____
9. _____   19. _____
10. _____

Getting Started

SI Reference Sheet

The International System of Units (SI) is accepted as the standard for measurement throughout most of the world. Frequently used SI units are listed in **Table 1** and some supplementary SI units in **Table 2.**

Table 1

	Frequently Used SI Units
Length	1 millimeter (mm) = 100 micrometers (μm) 1 centimeter (cm) = 10 millimeters (mm) 1 meter (m) = 100 centimeters (cm) 1 kilometer (km) = 1,000 meters (m) 1 light-year = 9,460,000,000,000 kilometers (km)
Area	1 square meter (m²) = 10,000 square centimeters (cm²) 1 square kilometer (km²) = 1,000,000 square meters (m²)
Volume	1 milliliter (mL) = 1 cubic centimeter (cm³) 1 liter (L) = 1,000 milliliters (mL)
Mass	1 gram (g) = 1,000 milligrams (mg) 1 kilogram (kg) = 1,000 grams (g) 1 metric ton = 1,000 kilograms (kg)
Time	1 s = 1 second

Table 2

Supplementary SI Units			
Measurement	**Unit**	**Symbol**	**Expressed in base units**
Energy	joule	J	$kg \cdot m^2/s^2$
Force	newton	N	$kg \cdot m/s^2$
Power	watt	W	$kg \cdot m^2/s^3$ or J/s
Pressure	pascal	Pa	$kg/m \cdot s^2$ or N · m

Sometimes quantities are measured using different SI units. In order to use them together in an equation, you must convert all of the quantities into the same unit. To convert, you multiply by a conversion factor. A conversion factor is a ratio that is equal to one. Make a conversion factor by building a ratio of equivalent units. Place the new units in the numerator and the old units in the denominator. For example, to convert 1.255 L to mL, multiply 1.255 L by the appropriate ratio as follows:

$$1.255 \text{ L} \times 1,000 \text{ mL}/1 \text{ L} = 1,255 \text{ mL}$$

The unit L cancels just as if it were a number.

Temperature measurements in SI often are made in degrees Celsius. Celsius temperature is a supplementary unit derived from the base unit kelvin. The Celsius scale (°C) has 100 equal graduations between the freezing temperature (0°C) and the boiling temperature of water (100°C). The following relationship exists between the Celsius and kelvin temperature scales:

$$K = °C + 273$$

SI Reference Sheet (continued)

To convert from °F to °C, you can:

1. For exact amounts, use the equation at the bottom of **Table 3**, or
2. For approximate amounts, find °F on the thermometer at the left of **Figure 1** and determine °C on the thermometer at the right.

Table 3

Figure 1

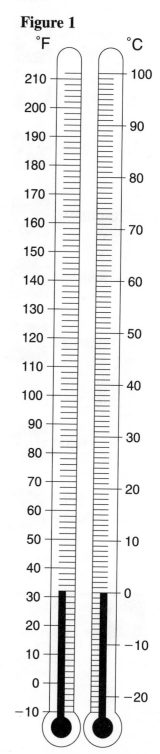

SI Metric to English Conversions			
	When you have:	**Multiply by:**	**To find:**
Length	inches	2.54	centimeters
	centimeters	0.39	inches
	feet	0.30	meters
	meters	3.28	feet
	yards	0.91	meters
	meters	1.09	yards
	miles	1.61	kilometers
	kilometers	0.62	miles
Mass and weight*	ounces	28.35	grams
	grams	0.04	ounces
	pounds	0.45	kilograms
	kilograms	2.20	pounds
	tons	0.91	metric tons
	metric tons	1.10	tons
	pounds	4.45	newtons
	newtons	0.23	pounds
Volume	cubic inches	16.39	cubic centimeters
	milliliters	0.06	cubic inches
	cubic feet	0.03	cubic meters
	cubic meters	35.31	cubic feet
	liters	1.06	quarts
	liters	0.26	gallons
	gallons	3.78	liters
Area	square inches	6.45	square centimeters
	square centimeters	0.16	square inches
	square feet	0.09	square meters
	square meters	10.76	square feet
	square miles	2.59	square kilometers
	square kilometers	0.39	square miles
	hectares	2.47	acres
	acres	0.40	hectares
Temperature	Fahrenheit	$\frac{5}{9}$ (°F − 32)	Celsius
	Celsius	$\frac{9}{5}$°C + 32	Fahrenheit

* Weight as measured in standard Earth gravity

Getting Started

SAFETY SYMBOLS

SAFETY SYMBOLS	HAZARD	EXAMPLES	PRECAUTION	REMEDY
DISPOSAL	Special disposal procedures need to be followed.	certain chemicals, living organisms	Do not dispose of these materials in the sink or trash can.	Dispose of wastes as directed by your teacher.
BIOLOGICAL	Organisms or other biological materials that might be harmful to humans	bacteria, fungi, blood, unpreserved tissues, plant materials	Avoid skin contact with these materials. Wear mask or gloves.	Notify your teacher if you suspect contact with material. Wash hands thoroughly.
EXTREME TEMPERATURE	Objects that can burn skin by being too cold or too hot	boiling liquids, hot plates, dry ice, liquid nitrogen	Use proper protection when handling.	Go to your teacher for first aid.
SHARP OBJECT	Use of tools or glassware that can easily puncture or slice skin	razor blades, pins, scalpels, pointed tools, dissecting probes, broken glass	Practice common-sense behavior and follow guidelines for use of the tool.	Go to your teacher for first aid.
FUME	Possible danger to respiratory tract from fumes	ammonia, acetone, nail polish remover, heated sulfur, moth balls	Make sure there is good ventilation. Never smell fumes directly. Wear a mask.	Leave foul area and notify your teacher immediately.
ELECTRICAL	Possible danger from electrical shock or burn	improper grounding, liquid spills, short circuits, exposed wires	Double-check setup with teacher. Check condition of wires and apparatus.	Do not attempt to fix electrical problems. Notify your teacher immediately.
IRRITANT	Substances that can irritate the skin or mucus membranes of the respiratory tract	pollen, moth balls, steel wool, fiber glass, potassium permanganate	Wear dust mask and gloves. Practice extra care when handling these materials.	Go to your teacher for first aid.
CHEMICAL	Chemicals that can react with and destroy tissue and other materials	bleaches such as hydrogen peroxide; acids such as sulfuric acid, hydrochloric acid; bases such as ammonia, sodium hydroxide	Wear goggles, gloves, and an apron.	Immediately flush the affected area with water and notify your teacher.
TOXIC	Substance may be poisonous if touched, inhaled, or swallowed	mercury, many metal compounds, iodine, poinsettia plant parts	Follow your teacher's instructions.	Always wash hands thoroughly after use. Go to your teacher for first aid.
OPEN FLAME	Open flame may ignite flammable chemicals, loose clothing, or hair	alcohol, kerosene, potassium permanganate, hair, clothing	Tie back hair. Avoid wearing loose clothing. Avoid open flames when using flammable chemicals. Be aware of locations of fire safety equipment.	Notify your teacher immediately. Use fire safety equipment if applicable.

 Eye Safety Proper eye protection should be worn at all times by anyone performing or observing science activities.

 Clothing Protection This symbol appears when substances could stain or burn clothing.

 Animal Safety This symbol appears when safety of animals and students must be ensured.

 Radioactivity This symbol appears when radioactive materials are used.

Student Laboratory and Safety Guidelines

Regarding Emergencies

- Inform the teacher immediately of *any* mishap—fire, injury, glassware breakage, chemical spills, and so forth.
- Follow your teacher's instructions and your school's procedures in dealing with emergencies.

Regarding Your Person

- Do NOT wear clothing that is loose enough to catch on anything and avoid sandals or open-toed shoes.
- Wear protective safety gloves, goggles, and aprons as instructed.
- Always wear safety goggles (not glasses) when using hazardous chemicals.
- Wear goggles throughout entire activity, cleanup, and handwashing.
- Keep your hands away from your face while working in the laboratory.
- Remove synthetic fingernails before working in the lab (these are highly flammable).
- Do NOT use hair spray, mousse, or other flammable hair products just before or during laboratory work where an open flame is used (they can ignite easily).
- Tie back long hair and loose clothing to keep them away from flames and equipment.
- Remove loose jewelry—chains or bracelets—while doing lab work.
- NEVER eat or drink while in the lab or store food in lab equipment or the lab refrigerator.
- Do NOT inhale vapors or taste, touch, or smell any chemical or substance unless instructed to do so by your teacher.

Regarding Your Work

- Read all instructions before you begin a laboratory or field activity. Ask questions if you do not understand any part of the activity.
- Work ONLY on activities assigned by your teacher.
- Do NOT substitute other chemicals/substances for those listed in your activity.
- Do NOT begin any activity until directed to do so by your teacher.
- Do NOT handle any equipment without specific permission.
- Remain in your own work area unless given permission by your teacher to leave it.
- Do NOT point heated containers—test tubes, flasks, and so forth—at yourself or anyone else.
- Do NOT take any materials or chemicals out of the classroom.
- Stay out of storage areas unless you are instructed to be there and are supervised by your teacher.
- NEVER work alone in the laboratory.
- When using dissection equipment, always cut away from yourself and others. Cut downward, never stabbing at the object.
- Handle living organisms or preserved specimens only when authorized by your teacher.
- Always wear heavy gloves when handling animals. If you are bitten or stung, notify your teacher immediately.

Regarding Cleanup

- Keep work and lab areas clean, limiting the amount of easily ignitable materials.
- Turn off all burners and other equipment before leaving the lab.
- Carefully dispose of waste materials as instructed by your teacher.
- Wash your hands thoroughly with soap and warm water after each activity.

Getting Started

Student Science Laboratory Safety Contract

I agree to:

- Act responsibly at all times in the laboratory.

- Follow all instructions given, orally or in writing, by my teacher.

- Perform only those activities assigned and approved by my teacher.

- Protect my eyes, face, hands, and body by wearing proper clothing and using protective equipment provided by my school.

- Carry out good housekeeping practices as instructed by my teacher.

- Know the location of safety and first aid equipment in the laboratory.

- Notify my teacher immediately of an emergency.

- NEVER work alone in the laboratory.

- NEVER eat or drink in the laboratory unless instructed to do so by my teacher.

- Handle living organisms or preserved specimens only when authorized by my teacher, and then, with respect.

- NEVER enter or work in a supply area unless instructed to do so and supervised by my teacher.

[This portion of the contract is to be kept by the student.]

[Return this portion to your teacher.]

I, _____, [print name] have read each of the statements in the Student Science Laboratory Safety Contract and understand these safety rules. I agree to abide by the safety regulations and any additional written or verbal instructions provided by the school district or my teacher. I further agree to follow all other written and verbal instructions given in class.

_____   _____

Student Signature   Date

I acknowledge that my child/ward has signed this contract in good faith.

_____   _____

Parent/Guardian Signature   Date

Relationships

Most students will agree that the longer they study for tests, the higher they score. In other words, test grades seem to be related to the amount of time spent studying. If two variables are related, one variable depends on the other. One variable is called the independent variable; the other is called the dependent variable. If test grades and study time are related, what is the independent variable—the test grades or the time spent studying?

One of the most simple types of relationships is a linear relationship. In linear relationships, the change in the dependent variable caused by a change in the independent variable can be determined from a graph. In this experiment you will investigate how a graph can be used to describe the relationship between the stretch of a rubber band and the force stretching it.

Strategy

You will measure the effect of increasing forces on the length of a rubber band.
You will graph the results of the experiment.
You will interpret the graph.

Materials

ring stand
ring clamp
several heavy books
3 rubber bands, equal lengths, different widths
2 plastic-coated wire ties, 10 cm and 30 cm long
metric ruler
100-g, 200-g, and 500-g masses

Procedure

1. Set up the ring stand, ring clamp, and books as shown in Figure 1.
2. Choose the narrowest rubber band. Securely attach the rubber band to the ring clamp with the 10-cm plastic-coated wire tie.
3. Measure the width of the rubber band. Record this value in Table 1 in the Data and Observations section.
4. Measure the length of the rubber band as it hangs from the ring clamp. Record this value in Table 1 as 0 mass.
5. Attach the 100-g mass to the bottom of the rubber band with the second wire tie. Measure the length of the stretched rubber band. Record this value in Table 1.
6. Remove the mass and attach the 200-g mass to the bottom of the rubber band. Measure the length of the stretched rubber band. Record this value in Table 1.

Figure 1

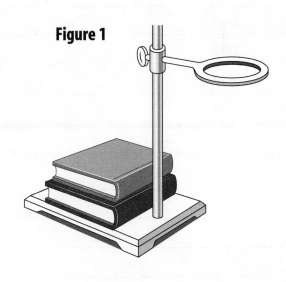

Laboratory Activity 1 (continued)

7. Remove the 200-g mass from the rubber band. Securely wrap the 100-g and 200-g masses together with the wire tie and tighten it. Attach the combined masses to the rubber band with the wire tie. Measure the length of the rubber band and record the value in Table 1.

8. Repeat measuring the lengths of the stretched rubber band for the 500-g mass and the combined masses of 600 g, 700 g, 800 g. Record the values in the data table.

9. Remove the rubber band.

10. Replace the rubber band with a slightly wider one. Hypothesize how the stretching of the wider rubber band will differ from that of the thinner one. Record your hypothesis in the Data and Observations section.

11. Repeat steps 3–9 for the second rubber band.

12. Replace the rubber band with the widest one and repeat steps 3–9 for the third rubber band.

Data and Observations

Table 1

Mass (g)	Length of rubber band (cm)		
	_____ mm width	_____ mm width	_____ mm width
0			
100			
200			
300			
500			
600			
700			
800			

1. Hypothesize how the stretching of a wider rubber band will differ from that of a thinner one.

_____

_____

_____

_____

Laboratory Activity 1 (continued)

2. In most experiments, the independent variable is plotted on the *x*-axis, which is the horizontal axis. The dependent variable is plotted on the *y*-axis, which is the vertical axis. In this experiment, the lengths of the rubber bands change as more mass is used to stretch them. The length of each of the rubber bands is the dependent variable. The mass that is used to stretch them is the independent variable. Use Graph 1 to plot the data for all three rubber bands. Plot the values of the masses causing the rubber bands to stretch on the *x*-axis. Plot the lengths of the rubber bands on the *y*-axis. Label the *x*-axis *Mass (g)* and the *y*-axis *Length (cm)*.

Graph 1

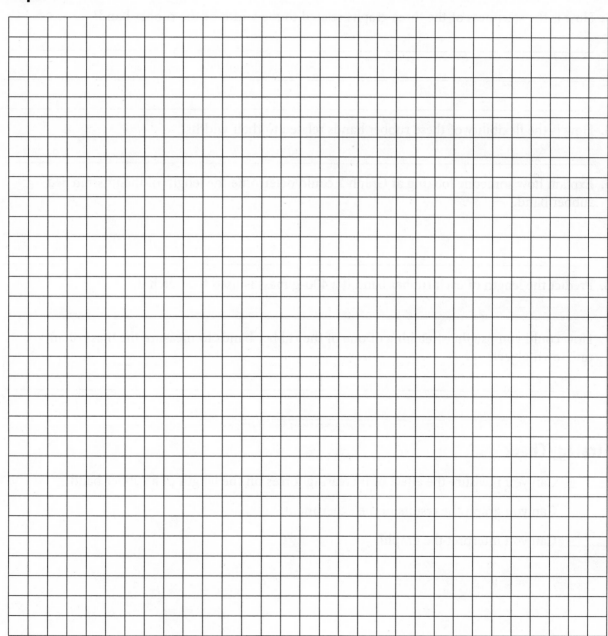

Laboratory Activity 1 (continued)

Questions and Conclusions

1. What do the graphs you made describe?

_____

_____

2. What does the steepness of the line of the graph measure?

_____

3. How is the steepness of the three graphs related to the width of the rubber band?

_____

_____

_____

4. How is the flexibility of these rubber bands related to their widths?

_____

5. Explain how someone looking at Graph 1 could determine the length of the unstretched rubber band.

_____

_____

6. Predict the length of each rubber band if a 400-g mass is used to stretch it.

_____

7. How could you use the stretching of one of the rubber bands to measure the mass of an unknown object?

_____

_____

Strategy Check

_____ Can you measure the effect of increasing forces on the length of a rubber band?

_____ Can you graph the results of the experiment?

_____ Can you interpret the graph?

No Need to Count Your Pennies

Chapter 1

Have you ever saved pennies, nickels, or dimes? If you have, you probably took them to the bank in paper wrappers provided by the bank. Tellers at the bank could take the time to open each roll and count the coins to determine their dollar value. However, counting is not necessary because tellers use a better system. They use the properties of the coins instead.

A penny, a nickel, and a dime each has a particular mass and thickness. Therefore, a roll of coins will have a certain mass and length. These two properties—mass and length of a roll of coins—are often used to determine the dollar value of the coins in the roll.

Strategy

You will develop measuring skills using a balance and a metric ruler.
You will use graphing skills to make interpretations about your data.
You will compare the relationships among the mass, length, and number of coins in a roll.

Materials

10 coins (all of the same type)
balance
metric ruler
roll of coins

Procedure

1. Using the balance, determine the mass of 1 coin, 2 coins, 3 coins, 4 coins, 6 coins, 8 coins, and 10 coins to the nearest 0.1 g. Record the masses in Table 1 in the Data and Observations section.

2. Measure the thickness of 1 coin, 2 coins, 3 coins, 4 coins, 6 coins, 8 coins, and 10 coins to the nearest 0.5 mm. See Figure 1. Record these values in the table.

3. Record the number of coins in the roll on the table. Use the balance to find the mass of the roll of coins. Measure the length of the roll. Record these values in the table.

Figure 1

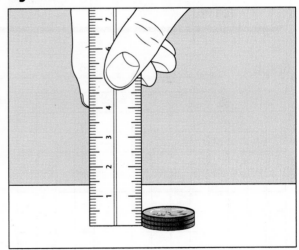

Laboratory Activity 2 (continued)

Data and Observations

1. Make two graphs of the information in Table 1. On Graph 1, show the number of coins on the x-axis and the mass of the coins on the y-axis. Graph 2 should compare the number of coins (x-axis) to the total thickness of the stacked coins (y-axis). Be sure to label each axis.
2. Draw a line connecting the points on each graph.

Table 1

Number of coins	Mass (g)	Thickness (mm)
1		
2		
3		
4		
6		
8		
10		
roll =		

Graph 1

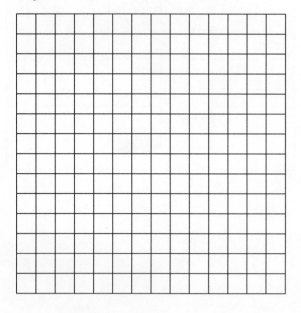

Graph 2

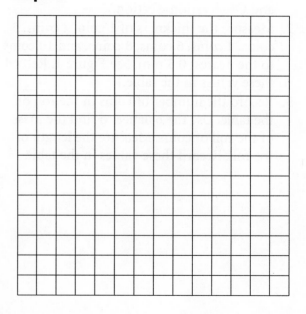

Laboratory Activity 2 (continued)

Questions and Conclusions

1. Describe the appearance of the curve or line in each graph.

_____

2. What errors could exist in your measurement of the mass and the length of the coin roll?

_____

_____

3. Which of the errors in question 2 would have real importance for a bank teller?

_____

_____

4. Do your data show a difference in the mass of different coins? Explain your answer.

_____

_____

_____

5. Do your data show a difference in the thickness of different coins? Explain your answer.

_____

_____

6. Could you use the mass of 1 coin to determine the mass of 2, 3, 4, 6, 8, and 10 coins? Why or why not?

_____

_____

_____

_____

Strategy Check

_____ Can you develop measuring skills using a balance and a metric ruler?

_____ Can you use graphing skills to make interpretations about your data?

_____ Can you compare the relationships among the mass, length, and number of coins in a roll?

Pushing People Around

When we push something, we unconsciously compensate for how much mass it has. We know that if an object has a larger mass it will require more force to get it moving and if it has a small mass it will require less force. But how much difference is there? In this experiment, we will see what variables affect acceleration.

Strategy

You will see what happens when you use a constant force to pull a skater.
You will examine the relationship between force, acceleration, and mass.

Materials

tape
meter stick
roller skates
skating safety equipment (helmet, pads)
spring balance
stopwatch

Procedure

1. Mark positions on the floor at intervals of 0 m, 5 m, 10 m, and 15 m with the tape. The floor should be smooth, straight, and level.

2. Have one student stand on the 0-m mark with the skates on. A second student stands behind the mark and holds the skater. The skater holds the spring balance by its hook.

3. The third student holds the other end of the spring balance and exerts a constant pulling force on the skater. When the skater is released, the puller must maintain a constant force throughout the distance. Measure the time to each of the marks. Record this in the Data and Observations section along with the spring balance readings at each mark.

4. Repeat steps 2 and 3 for two different skaters in order to vary the mass. Keep the force the same. Make sure the skaters hold their skates parallel and do not try to change direction during the trial.

5. Repeat steps 2, 3, and 4 with a different constant force. Use the same three skaters. Record these results in the Data and Observations section.

Laboratory Activity 1 (continued)

Data and Observations

Table 1

Trial	Roller Skater Distance, Trial 1		
	Distance (m)	Force (N)	Time (s)
1	5		
	10		
	15		
2	5		
	10		
	15		
3	5		
	10		
	15		

Table 2

Trial	Roller Skater Distance, Trial 2		
	Distance (m)	Force (N)	Time (s)
1	5		
	10		
	15		
2	5		
	10		
	15		
3	5		
	10		
	15		

Laboratory Activity 1 (continued)

Questions and Conclusions

1. Until the time of Galileo and Newton, people believed that, disregarding friction, a constant force was required to produce a constant speed. Do your observations confirm or reject this notion?

   _____

   _____

2. What happens to the speed as you proceed farther along the measured distance?

   _____

3. What happens to the rate of increase in speed—the acceleration—as you proceed farther along the measured distance?

   _____

4. When the force is the same, how does the acceleration depend upon the mass?

   _____

5. When the mass of the skater is the same, how does the acceleration depend upon the force?

   _____

6. Suppose a 4-N force is applied to the skater and no movement results. How can this be explained?

   _____

   _____

Strategy Check

_____ Can you pull someone with a constant force?

_____ Can you explain the relationship between force, mass, and acceleration?

Motion of a Bowling Ball

Chapter 2

It takes time to walk somewhere. Sometimes you move quickly, while other times you move slowly. Other objects might show variation in their movement as well. In this lab, you will graph the movement of a bowling ball and consider how its motion relates to other kinds of motion.

Strategy

You will make a distance versus time graph of a bowling ball as it rolls.
You will relate the motion of the bowling ball to other types of motion.

Materials

bowling ball
stopwatches (5–10)
large pillow

Procedure

1. Line up with other students at equally spaced distances of 1m. Your teacher will mark the distances.
2. At the far end of the hall, set up the pillow or other large, soft object. This will prevent the ball from rolling too far.
3. Start your stopwatch when your teacher rolls the ball slowly.
4. When the ball passes you, stop your stopwatch. As the ball passes the other students, they will do the same.

5. Record all of your times in Table 1.
6. Clear your stopwatch to prepare for another trial. This time, your teacher will roll the ball faster.
7. Record your times in Table 2.
8. Graph the data for both tables, putting the data from Table 1 into Graph 1, and the data from Table 2 into Graph 2. Place the distance on the vertical axis, and the time on the horizontal axis.

Data and Observations

Trial 1	
Distance	**Time**
0 m	
1 m	
2 m	
3 m	
4 m	
5 m	

Trial 2	
Distance	**Time**
0 m	
1 m	
2 m	
3 m	
4 m	
5 m	

Laboratory Activity 2 (continued)

Graph 1

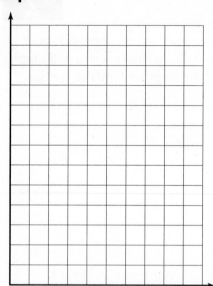

Graph 2

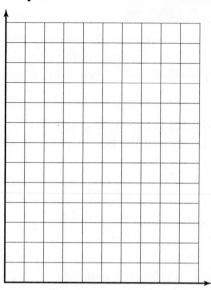

Questions and Conclusions

1. What do you notice about the graphs of the two trials?

_____

_____

2. On a distance versus time graph, what does the slope of the line tell you?

_____

_____

3. On a distance versus time graph, what does a flat (horizontal) line mean?

_____

4. Imagine a bowling ball dropped from a great height. How would the motion of this bowling ball relate to the bowling balls in the lab?

_____

_____

_____

5. What was the speed of the bowling ball in the first trial? In the second trial?

_____

_____

Laboratory Activity 2 (continued)

6. What distance did the bowling balls travel? What is their displacement?

_____

_____

7. How are distance and displacement related?

_____

_____

Strategy Check

_____ Can you graph the speed of an object in motion?

LAB 1 Laboratory Activity

Projectile Motion

Chapter 3

What do a volleyball, baseball, tennis ball, soccer ball, and football have in common? Each is used in a sport and each is a projectile after it is tapped, thrown, kicked, or hit. A projectile is any object that is thrown or shot into the air. If air resistance is ignored, the only force acting on a projectile is the force of gravity.

The path followed by a projectile is called a trajectory. Figure 1a shows the shape of the trajectory of a toy rocket. Because the force of gravity is the only force acting on it, the toy rocket has an acceleration of 9.80 m/s² downward. However, the motion of the projectile is upward and then downward. Figure 1b shows the size and direction of the vertical velocity of a toy rocket at different moments along its trajectory. The rocket's velocity upward begins to decrease immediately after launch and the rocket begins to slow down. The rocket continues to slow down. And then, for an instant at the highest point of its trajectory, it stops moving because its velocity upward is zero. As the rocket begins to fall, its velocity begins to increase downward.

As you can see, the shape of the upward trajectory of the rocket is a mirror-image of the shape of its downward trajectory. Can the trajectory of a toy rocket be used to learn something about the motion of a projectile? In this experiment you will find out.

Strategy

You will measure the flight times of a projectile.
You will analyze the flight times of a projectile.

Materials 🥽

toy water rocket and launcher
bucket of water
3 stopwatches

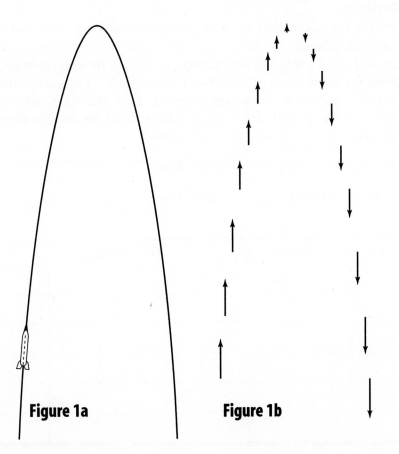

Figure 1a   **Figure 1b**

Laboratory Activity 1 (continued)

Procedure

1. Wear goggles during this experiment.
2. Fill the water rocket to the level line shown on the rocket's body. Always fill the rocket to the same level during each flight in the experiment.
3. Attach the pump/launcher to the rocket as shown in the manufacturer's directions.
4. Pump the pump/launcher 10 times. **CAUTION:** *Do not exceed 20 pumps or the maximum number suggested by the manufacturer, whichever is lower. Be sure to hold the rocket and pump/launcher so that the rocket is not directed toward yourself or another person.*
5. Launch the rocket vertically. Predict the time for the rocket to rise to its highest point, and the time for it to fall back to Earth. Now predict these times if the rocket is pumped 15 times. Record your predictions as time up and time down in the Data and Observations section.
6. Retrieve the rocket. Fill the rocket with water as in step 2. Pump the pump/launcher 10 times. Record the number of pumps in Table 1.
7. At a given signal to the timers, launch the rocket. Your teacher will have timers measure specific parts of the flight using stopwatches. Record the values measured by the timers as total time, time up, and time down in Table 1.
8. Repeat steps 6 and 7 twice.
9. Repeat steps 6 and 7 three more times, increasing the number of pumps to 15 for each launch. **CAUTION:** *Do not exceed the maximum number of pumps suggested by the manufacturer.*

Data and Observations

1. Calculate the average total time, time up, and average time down for the two sets of launches. Record these values in Table 2.
2. Use Graph 1 to construct a bar graph comparing the average time up, average total time, and average time down for the two sets of launches. Plot the number of pumps used in each set of launches on the *x*-axis and the three average times (up, total, down) on the *y*-axis. Label the *x*-axis *Number of pumps* and the *y*-axis *Time (s)*. Clearly label the average time up, average total time, and average time down for each set of launches.

10 pumps—Prediction of time up: _____; time down _____

15 pumps—Prediction of time up: _____; time down _____

Table 1

Number of pumps	Total time (s)	Time up (s)	Time down (s)

Laboratory Activity 1 (continued)

Table 2

Number of pumps	Average total time (s)	Average time up (s)	Average time down (s)

Graph 1

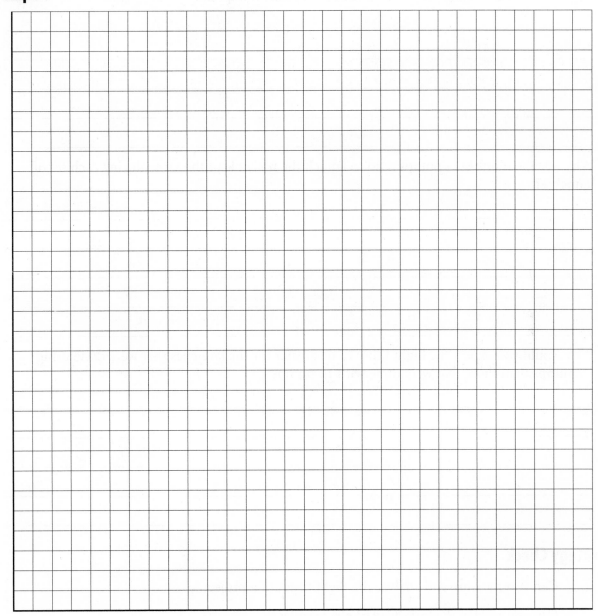

Laboratory Activity 1 (continued)

Questions and Conclusions

1. How well did your predictions agree with the measured times?

_____

_____

_____

2. Do your graphs support the statement that the time for a projectile to reach its highest point is equal to the time for the projectile to fall back to Earth? Explain.

_____

_____

_____

_____

_____

3. Why was the number of pumps used to launch the rocket kept the same during each set of launches?

_____

_____

_____

_____

4. Why would you expect the flight times to be greater for the launches that were done using 15 pumps than those that were done with 10 pumps?

_____

_____

_____

_____

_____

Strategy Check

_____ Can you measure and analyze the flight times of a projectile?

_____ Can you predict the trajectory of a projectile?

Velocity and Momentum

LAB 2 Laboratory Activity

As you know, you can increase the speed of a shopping cart by pushing harder on its handles. You can also increase its speed by pushing on the handles for a longer time. Both ways will increase the momentum of the cart. How is the momentum of an object related to the time that a force acts on it? In this experiment, you will investigate that question.

Strategy

You will observe the effect of a net force on a cart.
You will measure the velocity of the cart at various times.
You will determine the momentum of the cart.
You will relate the momentum of the cart and the time during which the force acted on it.

Materials

utility clamp
ring stand
2 plastic-coated wire ties (1 short, 1 long)
pulley
metric balance
momentum cart
2–3 rubber bands
1-m length of string

100-g mass
3–4 books
plastic foam sheet
meterstick
masking tape
stopwatch/timer
felt-tip marker

Procedure

1. Attach the utility clamp to the ring stand. Using the short plastic-coated wire tie, attach the pulley to the clamp.
2. Use the metric balance to find the mass of the cart. Record this value in the Data and Observations section on the line provided.
3. Wrap the rubber bands around the cart lengthwise.
4. Tie one end of the string around the rubber bands as shown in Figure 1. Tie a loop at the opposite end of the string. Pass the string over the pulley.

5. Wrap the long plastic-coated wire tie securely around the 100-g mass. Attach the mass to the loop on the string with the wire tie.
6. Place the ring stand near the edge of the table. Adjust the position of the pulley so that the string is parallel to the table top as shown in Figure 2. Be sure that the 100-g mass can fall freely to the floor. Place several heavy books on the base of the ring stand.
7. Place a plastic foam sheet beneath the mass.

Figure 1

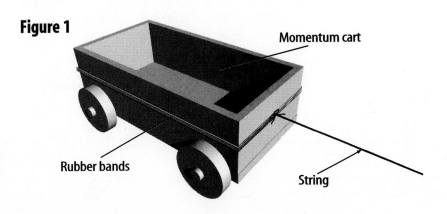

Momentum cart

Rubber bands

String

Laboratory Activity 2 (continued)

Figure 2

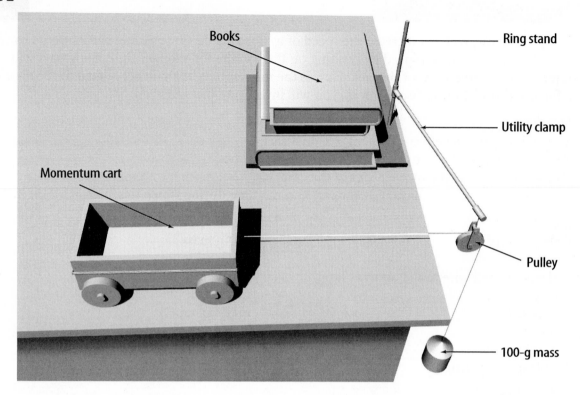

Books

Ring stand

Utility clamp

Momentum cart

Pulley

100-g mass

8. Pull the cart back until the 100-g mass is about 80 cm above the foam sheet. Have your lab partner place a strip of masking tape on the table marking the position of the front wheels. Release the cart. Observe the motion of the cart. Record your observations on a separate sheet of paper. **CAUTION:** *Have your partner stop the cart before it runs into the pulley.*

9. Using the marker, label the strip of masking tape *Starting Line*. Use the meterstick to measure a distance of 0.20 m from the starting line. Place a strip of masking tape on the table to mark this distance.

Be sure to have the strip of masking tape parallel to the starting line. Label the strip of masking tape *0.20 m*. Measure and label distances of 0.40 m and 0.60 m in the same manner. See Figure 3.

10. Pull the cart back with one hand until its front wheels are on the starting line. Hold the stopwatch in the other hand. Release the cart and immediately start the stopwatch. Measure the time for the front wheels to cross the 0.20-m line. **CAUTION:** *Have your partner stop the cart before it reaches the pulley.* Record the distance and time values as Trial 1 in Table 1.

Figure 3

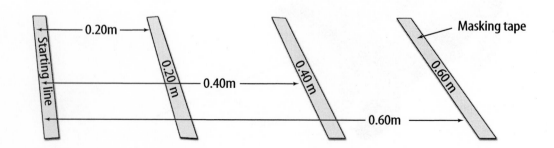

Starting line

0.20m

0.20 m

0.40m

0.40 m

Masking tape

0.60 m

0.60m

Laboratory Activity 2 (continued)

11. Repeat step 10 twice. Record the values as Trials 2 and 3.
12. Repeat steps 10 and 11 to measure the time for the front wheels to cross the 0.40-m and 0.60-m lines.

Data and Observations

Table 1

Distance (m)	Time (s)		
	Trial 1	Trial 2	Trial 3

Table 2

Distance (m)	Average time (s)	Average velocity (m/s)	Final velocity (m/s)	Momentum (g·m/s)

Graph 1

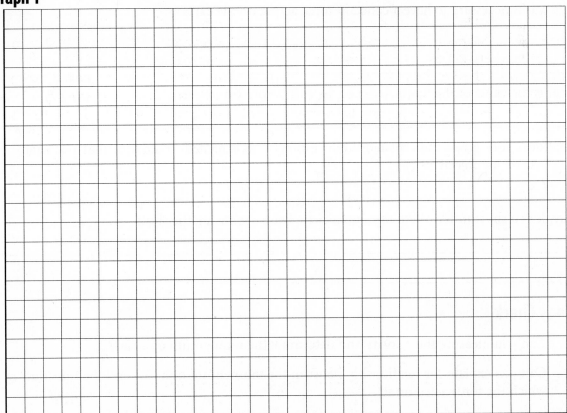

Laboratory Activity 2 (continued)

1. Calculate the average times for the cart to travel 0.20 m, 0.40 m, and 0.60 m. Record these values in Table 2.
2. Calculate the average velocity for each distance by dividing distance traveled by average time. Record these values in Table 2.
3. Because the cart started from rest and had a constant force acting on it, the velocity of the cart at a given distance from the starting line is equal to twice its average velocity for that distance. That is, the velocity of the cart as it crossed the 0.20-m line is twice the value of the average velocity that you calculated for 0.20 m. Calculate the velocity of the cart as it crossed the 0.20-m line, the 0.40-m line, and the 0.60-m line. Record these values in Table 2.
4. Calculate the momentum of the cart as it crossed the 0.20-m, 0.40-m, and 0.60-m lines by multiplying the mass of the cart by its velocity. Record these values in Table 2.
5. Use Graph 1 to make a graph of your data. Plot the average time on the *x*-axis and the momentum on the *y*-axis. Label the *x*-axis *Time (s)* and the *y*-axis *Momentum* (P).

   Step 1. Mass of cart: _____ g

   Step 8. Observation of motion of a cart:

   _____

   _____

Questions and Conclusions

1. What force caused the cart to accelerate?

   _____

2. Why was it necessary to have a constant force acting on the cart?

   _____

   _____

3. What is the value of the momentum of the cart before you released it?

   _____

4. What does your graph indicate about how momentum is related to the time that a constant force acts on an object?

   _____

5. Why does a shot-putter rotate through a circle before releasing the shot?

   _____

   _____

Strategy Check

_____ Can you measure the velocity and determine the momentum of a cart?

_____ Can you explain the relationship between the momentum of a cart and the time during which the force acted on it?

The Energy of a Pendulum

When you ride on a playground swing, you have energy. Any moving object has kinetic energy, which is energy due to motion. Kinetic energy depends on the velocity and the mass of the moving object. Increasing the mass on the swing by holding something in your lap or your velocity by swinging faster increases your kinetic energy.

An object at rest may also have energy. When an object is held in a position where it would move if released, it has energy of position called potential energy. When you begin to swing, a friend may pull your swing back and up. See Figure 1. Before your friend releases the swing, you are at rest and have potential energy. In this position, you are not moving, so you have no kinetic energy. But you could move if released, so you have potential energy. As long as the swing is in a position where it can move, you have potential energy. After your friend releases the swing, you have both potential energy and kinetic energy. See Figure 2.

Figure 1

Figure 2

Figure 3

If you were to sit in the swing and allow it to hang straight down from its supports, you would not move. You are not held in a position where you can move. With reference only to the swing, you have no potential energy and no kinetic energy. See Figure 3.

A swing is one example of a pendulum. Many clocks have a swinging mass, or pendulum, to move the hands. A pendulum can have both potential energy and kinetic energy, depending on its position. How much energy depends also on its mass and velocity. A pendulum hanging straight down, at rest, has neither potential energy nor kinetic energy.

How do potential energy and kinetic energy change as a pendulum swings? Write your hypothesis in the Data and Observations section.

Strategy

You will construct a pendulum.
You will explain how a pendulum behaves.
You will describe the potential energy and kinetic energy of a pendulum.

Materials

ring
strings, 20 cm and 30 cm long (2)
ring stand

sinkers, different sizes (2)
metric ruler
watch with second hand

Laboratory Activity 1 (continued)

Procedure

1. Set up the ring and ring stand. Use the metric ruler to adjust the ring to a height of 35 cm above the table or desk.

Figure 4

2. Securely tie the short string to the smaller sinker. Measure 15 cm along the string. Tie the string at this point to the ring as shown in Figure 4.

3. Allow the pendulum to hang at rest. Consider the energy of the Pendulum—potential, kinetic, or both. Record your observations in the Data and Observations section.

4. Hold the pendulum above the table to form a small angle with the ring stand. Record your observations about the pendulum's energy.

5. From the raised position, release the pendulum and allow it to swing for exactly two minutes. Count the number of full swings (back and forth) during the two minutes. Record this information in the Data and Observations section.

6. Run a second trial, counting the swings for another two minutes. Record this information in the data table.

7. Do three other sets of trials. Vary either the length of the string or the size of the sinker as indicated in the data table. Record your information in the data table.

8. Calculate the average number of swings for each two-minute trial. Record this information in the data table.

Data and Observations

Hypothesis:

_____

_____

_____

_____

Step 3 observations:

_____

_____

_____

_____

Laboratory Activity 1 (continued)

Step 4 observations:

_____

_____

_____

_____

Pendulum		Similarities and differences		
String length (cm)	Trial 1	Trial 1	Trial 2	Average
15	small			
15	large			
25	small			
25	large			

Questions and Conclusions

1. What type of energy does the pendulum have when it is hanging straight down?

_____

2. What type of energy does the pendulum have if it is held at a right angle to the stand?

_____

3. What force acted on the pendulum when it was released from its raised position?

_____

4. Which string length caused the pendulum to swing more times in two minutes? Which sinker size caused the pendulum to swing more times in two minutes?

_____

_____

_____

5. Describe the best method for increasing the number of swings of a pendulum during a set time period.

_____

_____

Laboratory Activity 1 (continued)

6. Figure 5 represents a pendulum in motion. Look at the diagram and label it as indicated.
   a. Write the letter P at the position of maximum potential energy.
   b. Write the letter K at the position of maximum kinetic energy.
   c. Write the letter I at the position where kinetic energy is increased.
   d. Write the letter D at the position where kinetic energy is decreased.

Figure 5

Strategy Check

_____ Can you explain how a pendulum behaves?

_____ Can you describe the potential energy of a pendulum?

_____ Can you describe the kinetic energy of a pendulum?

Laboratory Activity 2

Causing Friction

When you kick a soccer ball along the ground, you know that when you stop kicking the ball will eventually roll to a stop. What happens to the kinetic energy of the ball as it slows down? The law of conservation of energy states that energy cannot be created or destroyed. Therefore, the kinetic energy of the soccer ball does not just disappear; it changes form. As the ball rolls over the ground, friction causes some of its kinetic energy to change into thermal energy. Friction between the ball and the ground causes the ball to slow down and eventually stop. In this experiment, you will examine how different types of surfaces affect the amount of friction produced.

Strategy

You will predict what types of surfaces produce the least friction.
You will observe how friction affects the kinetic energy of a toy car.

Materials

books (2)   coarse sandpaper (3 sheets)
meterstick   strip of rough carpeting
toy car   pillowcase
masking tape

Procedure

1. Place a book on top of a smooth, hard surface such as a table or an uncarpeted floor. Lean a second book against the first to form a ramp.

Figure 1

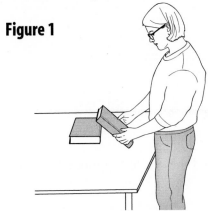

2. Use the meterstick to measure the height of the ramp. See Figure 1. Record the height in the Data and Observations section.

3. Do you think hard surfaces or soft surfaces will reduce the kinetic energy of a toy car more quickly? Rough surfaces or smooth surfaces? Record your predictions in the Data and Observations section.

4. Place the car at the top of the ramp and release it. Measure the distance between the bottom of the ramp and the spot where the car stopped moving. Record this distance in the table in the Data and Observations section. Repeat this step two more times. Use the meterstick to make sure that you release the car from the same height each time.

5. Tape the pieces of sandpaper together into a strip. Place the strip at the bottom of your ramp. See Figure 2. Repeat Step 4.

Figure 2

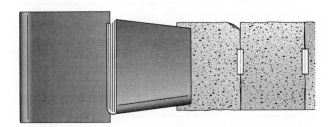

Laboratory Activity 2 (continued)

6. Use your fingers to brush ridges into the carpet's surface. Remove the sandpaper from the bottom of your ramp and replace it with the carpeting. Repeat Step 4.

7. Fold the pillowcase lengthwise into thirds. Place it on top of the carpeting at the bottom of your ramp.
   Smooth out any wrinkles in the fabric with your hands. Repeat Step 4.

8. Calculate the average distance the car traveled on each surface. Record your calculations in the Data Table.

Data and Observations

Height of ramp: _____

Predict what type of surfaces—hard or soft, smooth or rough—will reduce the kinetic energy of the car the quickest?

_____

Surface	Distance Moved by Car (cm)			Distance Moved by Car (cm)
	Trial 1	Trial 2	Trial 3	
Floor or table (hard, smooth)				
Floor or table (hard, rough)				
Floor or table (soft, rough)				
Pillowcase (soft, smooth)				

Questions and Conclusions

1. What type of surface (hard or soft, smooth or rough) provided the greatest amount of friction? Explain how you know.

_____

_____

2. What type of surface provided the least amount of friction?

_____

_____

Laboratory Activity 2 (continued)

3. What happened to the kinetic energy of the car after the car left the ramp?

_____

_____

_____

4. Why was it important that the ramp be the same height in each trial?

_____

_____

_____

_____

5. Describe how you could determine the gravitational potential energy of the car at the top of the ramp.

_____

_____

_____

6. Examine the data in your table. Than predict the distance the car would move if you placed a layer of gravel at the bottom of your ramp. Explain how the data helped you make your prediction.

_____

_____

_____

7. Predict whether a hockey puck would move a greater distance over smooth ice or over rough ice. Explain how you used the data in your table to make your prediction.

_____

_____

_____

Strategy Check

_____ Can you predict what types of surfaces will produce the least friction?

_____ Can you observe how friction affects kinetic energy?

Balanced Levers

In general, a lever is a bar that is free to turn about a pivot point called a fulcrum. When a lever is balanced horizontally, the following relationship exists:

$$output\ force \times output\ arm = input\ force \times input\ arm$$

This equation is called the law of the lever.

You can use the principle of balanced levers to construct a mobile. Each of the dowel rods you will use in constructing your mobile acts as a lever. The point where each string supports a dowel rod is the fulcrum of the lever. The weights that you hang from the dowel rods to keep the lever in balance act on the objects as input and output forces. The distances between the objects and the fulcrum correspond to the input arm and output arm of the balanced lever.

Strategy

You will design and construct a mobile.
You will show that each lever in your mobile obeys the law of the lever.

Materials 🖐 🥽

string
meterstick
4 wooden dowel rods (one 50 cm long, the others at various shorter lengths)
various objects of different weights (paper clips, keys, etc.)
metric spring scale (calibrated in newtons)

Procedure

1. Tie a piece of string near the center of the 50 cm dowel. Anchor the other end of the string to the tabletop or ceiling, if possible. Allow room below this dowel to add objects to the mobile.

2. Weigh each object that you plan to use in constructing your mobile. Record the weights of the objects in Table 1. Be sure to include the smaller dowel rods when you weigh the objects.

3. Use the string and remaining rods to construct the mobile. You may use any design. However, the main lever (50-cm rod) and any other dowels you use must be balanced horizontally. See Figure 1.

4. When you are finished, measure the distance in mm from each hanging object to the fulcrum of each lever. When recording these distances in Table 2, choose one distance on the balanced lever as the output arm and the other as the input arm. Thus, the weight of the object hanging from the output arm is the output force. The weight of the object hanging from the input arm is the input force.

Figure 1

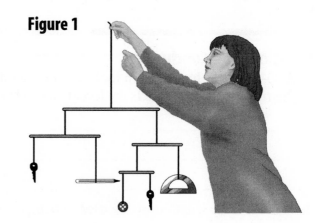

Laboratory Activity 1 (continued)

Data and Observations

For each lever, calculate the product of the output force and the output arm and the product of the input force and the input arm. Record your calculations in Table 2. Use your calculations to support the law of the lever.

Table 1

Object	Weight (N)	Object	Weight (N)

Table 2

Lever	Input arm (mm)	Input force (N)	Product (N × mm)	Output arm (mm)	Output force (N)	Product (N × mm)
A						
B						
C						
D						

Questions and Conclusions

1. A 25-N weight hangs 10 cm to the left of the fulcrum of a lever. A 15-N weight hangs 12 cm to the right of the fulcrum. Is the lever balanced? How do you know?

_____

_____

_____

2. How does the length of string used to hang the objects affect their position on the lever?

_____

_____

_____

Laboratory Activity 1 (continued)

3. When is an equal arm balance an example of a balanced lever?

_____

_____

_____

4. For the balanced levers shown in Figure 2, use the law of the levers to fill in the missing data for **a** and **b**.

Figure 2

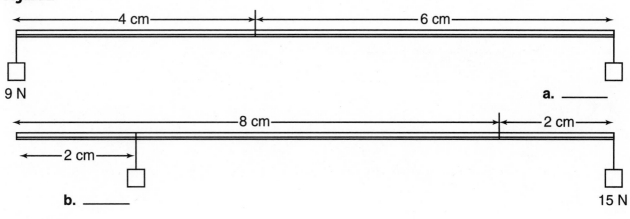

Strategy Check

_____ Can you design and construct a working mobile?

_____ Can you show that each lever in your mobile obeys the law of the lever?

Pulleys

If you have ever raised or lowered a flag or slatted blinds, you used a simple machine called a pulley. As you recall, simple machines can change direction of a force and multiply either the size of the effort force or the distance that the resistance force moves.

A single fixed pulley is a pulley that can't move up and down. As you can see in Figure 1, a fixed pulley is actually a lever in the form of a circle. Can you locate the effort arm and the resistance arm in a single fixed pulley?

Figure 1

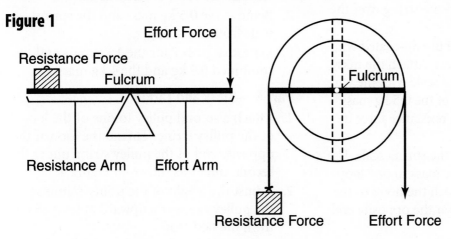

A series of pulleys is called a block and tackle. You may have seen a block and tackle in an auto repair shop. It sometimes is used to lift car engines. Look at the block and tackle shown in Figure 2. Can you locate a single fixed pulley in the block and tackle?

Figure 2

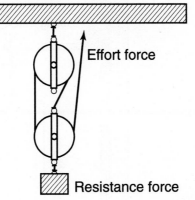

Strategy

You will perform work using a single fixed pulley.

You will construct a block and tackle and per form work with it.

You will compare the properties of a single fixed pulley and a block and tackle.

Materials

utility clamp
ring stand
plastic-coated wire ties, 10 cm and 30 cm long
2 pulleys
meterstick
1-m length of cotton string
masking tape
metric spring scale
0.5-kg and 1-kg standard masses

Laboratory Activity 2 (continued)

Procedure

Part A—Single Fixed Pulley

1. Attach the utility clamp to the top of a ring stand. Use the short plastic-coated wire tie to attach one of the pulleys to the utility clamp. Attach a meterstick to the ring stand with tape. See Figure 3.

2. Tie a small loop at each end of the 1-m length of string. Thread the string over the pulley.

3. Tightly wrap the second plastic-coated wire tie around the 0.5 kg mass. Attach the mass to the hook of the spring scale with the wire tie. Measure the weight of the 0.5 kg mass. Record this value as the resistance force in Table 1.

4. Remove the mass from the spring scale. Use the wire tie to attach the mass to one loop of the pulley string. Attach the hook of the spring scale to the loop at the opposite end of the string.

5. Slowly pull straight down on the spring scale to raise the mass. Measure the force needed to raise the mass 15 cm. Record this value as the effort force in Table 1.

6. Lower the mass to the table top. As you again pull down on the spring scale, measure the distance the spring scale moves as you raise the mass a distance of 15 cm. Record this value as the effort distance in Table 1.

7. Remove the 0.5 kg mass and the spring scale from the string.

8. Repeat steps 4–7 for the 1 kg mass and the combined 0.5 kg and the 1 kg masses.

Part B—Block and Tackle

1. Attach a second pulley to one of the loops of the pulley string. Thread the loop at the opposite end of the pulley string under the second pulley as shown in Figure 4.

2. Adjust the height of the utility clamp so the pulley can move upward at least 25 cm from the table top.

Figure 3

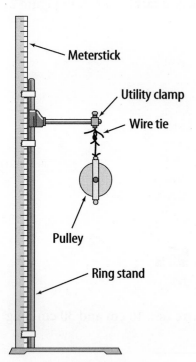

Figure 4

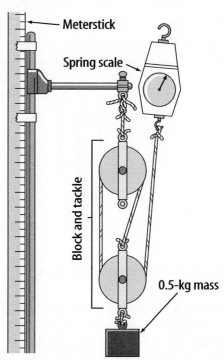

Laboratory Activity 2 (continued)

3. Wrap the plastic wire tie securely around the 0.5 kg mass. Use the spring scale to measure its weight. Record this value as the resistance force in Table 2. Attach the mass to the second pulley.

4. Attach the spring scale to the loop on the free end of the string.

5. Slowly pull straight up on the spring scale to raise the mass as shown in Figure 4. Measure the force needed to raise the mass 15 cm. Record this value as the effort distance in Table 2.

6. Lower the mass to the table top. As you again pull up on the spring scale, measure the distance the spring scale moves as you raise the mass a distance of 15 cm. Record this value as the effort distance in Table 2.

7. Remove the 0.5 kg mass from the pulley and the spring scale from the string.

8. Repeat steps 4–7 for the 1 kg mass and the combined 0.5 kg and 1 kg masses.

Data and Observations

1. Use Graph 1 to construct a bar graph comparing the effort force of the single fixed pulley, the effort force of the block and tackle, and the resistance force for each of the three masses. Plot the value of the masses on the *x* axis and the force on the *y* axis. Label the *x* axis *Mass (kg)* and the *y* axis *Force (N)*. Clearly label the bars that represent the values of the effort force of the single fixed pulley, the effort force of the block and tackle, and the resistance force.

2. Use Graph 2 to construct a bar graph comparing the effort distance of the single fixed pulley, the effort distance of the block and tackle, and the resistance distance for each of the three masses. Plot the value of the masses on the *x* axis and the distance on the *y* axis. Label the *x* axis *Mass (kg)* and the *y* axis *Distance (cm)*. Clearly label the bars that represent the values of the effort distance of the single fixed pulley, the effort distance of the block and tackle, and the resistance distance.

3. Work input is the work done by you. Work input can be calculated using the following equation.

Work input = Effort force × Effort distance

If the force is measured in newtons (N) and the distance is measured in meters (m), work will be expressed in joules (J). Calculate the work input for the pulley and the block and tackle for each mass. Record the values in Table 3.

4. Work output is the work done by the machine. Work output can be calculated using the following equation.

Work output = Resistance force × Resistance distance

If the force is measured in newtons (N) and the distance is measured in meters (m), work will be expressed in joules (J). Calculate the work output for the pulley and the block and tackle for each mass. Record the values in Table 3.

5. The efficiency of a machine is a measure of how the work output of a machine compares with the work input. The efficiency of a machine can be calculated using the following equation.

Efficiency = Work output/Work input × 100%

Use this equation to calculate the efficiency of the single fixed pulley and the efficiency of the block and tackle in raising each mass. Record these values in Table 4.

Laboratory Activity 2 (continued)

Table 1

Mass (kg)	Resistance force (N)	Effort force (N)	Resistance distance (cm)	Effort distance (cm)
0.5			15.0	
1.0			15.0	
1.5			15.0	

Table 2

Mass (kg)	Resistance force (N)	Effort force (N)	Resistance distance (cm)	Effort distance (cm)
0.5			15.0	
1.0			15.0	
1.5			15.0	

Table 3

Mass (kg)	Single fixed pulley		Block and tackle	
	Work input (J)	Work output (J)	Work input (J)	Work output (J)
0.5				
1.0				
1.5				

Table 4

Mass (kg)	Efficiency (%)	
	Single fixed pulley	Block and tackle
0.5		
1.0		
1.5		

Laboratory Activity 2 (continued)

Graph 1

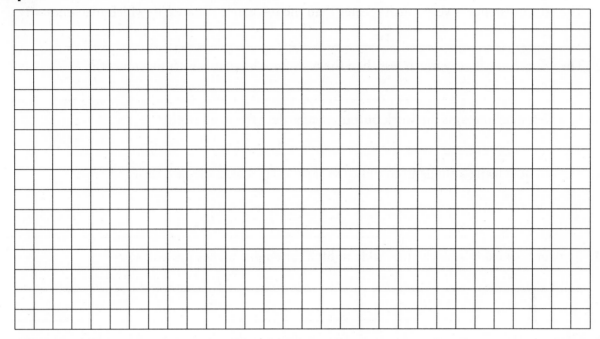

Graph 2

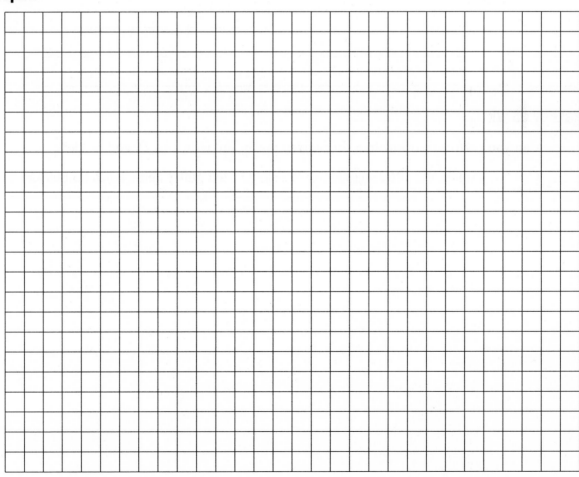

Laboratory Activity 2 (continued)

Questions and Conclusions

1. The effort distance is very much greater than the resistance distance in which machines(s)?

   _____

2. The effort force is very much less than the resistance force in which machine(s)?

   _____

3. In which machine(s) is the work output greater than the work input?

   _____

4. Explain how using a single fixed pulley to raise a flag makes the task easier.

   _____

   _____

5. Explain how using a block and tackle to lift a car engine makes the task easier.

   _____

   _____

6. Compare the efficiencies of the single fixed pulley and the block and tackle. Why would you expect the block and tackle to be less efficient than the single fixed pulley?

   _____

   _____

   _____

Strategy Check

_____ Can you perform work with a single fixed pulley and with a block and tackle?

_____ Can you explain the differences between a single fixed pulley and a block and tackle?

Specific Heats of Metals

The amount of heat needed to change the temperature of a metal is much less than that needed to change the temperature of a similar amount of other materials. You probably were aware of this fact if you ever tried to cool a can of soft drink quickly in the freezer. Metal cans tend to cool more quickly than their contents.

A measure of how much energy is needed to change the temperature of a material is called specific heat. The specific heat, *C*, is the amount of heat needed to change the temperature of 1 kilogram of a substance by 1 degree Celsius. As you recall, the specific heat of water is 4190 J/kg•°C. The specific heat of a substance is a physical property of that substance. Therefore, a substance can be identified by its specific heat.

Strategy

You will use a calorimeter to determine the specific heat of a piece of metal. You will identify the metal by its specific heat.

Materials

250-mL beaker
one-hole paper punch
metric balance
paper towels
2 plastic cups with lids

plastic pipette
rubber band
test tube, thick walled
test-tube holder

test-tube rack
thermometer
sample of unknown metal X, Y, or Z
water

Procedure

Part A—Building a Calorimeter

1. Place about 50 mL of water in the 250-mL beaker and allow the temperature of the water to come to room temperature.

2. Punch a hole for the thermometer in one of the lids of the plastic cups with a paper punch.

3. Wrap a rubber band around one of the plastic cups.

4. Place this cup inside the second plastic cup. Assemble the calorimeter as shown in Figure 1.

5. Measure the mass of the calorimeter. Record this value in the Data and Observations section.

Figure 1

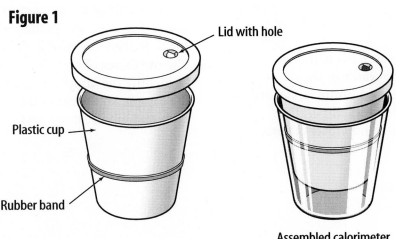

Lid with hole

Plastic cup

Rubber band

Assembled calorimeter

Laboratory Activity 1 (continued)

Part B—Measuring Specific Heat of Metals

1. Use the plastic pipette to add 5 pipette-fuls of room-temperature water to the calorimeter.

2. Measure the mass of the calorimeter and water. Record this value in the Data and Observations section.

3. Measure the mass of the sample of unknown metal. Record this value in Table 1.

4. Place the piece of metal in the test tube. Use the test-tube holder to place the test tube containing the metal into the boiling water bath prepared by your teacher. Note the time.

5. After ten minutes, measure the temperature of the water in the calorimeter with the thermometer. Remove the thermometer. Place the calorimeter on a paper towel on a flat surface and remove its lid.

6. Measure the temperature of the boiling water bath using the thermometer provided by your teacher. Record this value as the *temperature of metal* in the Data and Observations section.

7. Using the test-tube holder, carefully remove the test tube containing the sample from the boiling water bath. **CAUTION:** *The test tube and its contents are extremely hot. Avoid touching the test tube or the piece of metal.*

8. Quickly slide the piece of hot metal into the calorimeter. Place the test tube in the test-tube rack.

9. Immediately cover the calorimeter with its lid and insert the thermometer into the calorimeter.

10. Gently swirl the water. Measure the temperature of the water in the calorimeter for several minutes. Record the value of the *highest* temperature reading in the Data and Observations section.

11. Calculate the mass of the water that you added to the calorimeter by subtracting the mass of the empty calorimeter from the calorimeter and water. Record this value in Table 1.

12. Calculate the temperature change in the water. Record this value in Table 1.

13. The heat gained by the water can be determined by the following equation.
$$Q = C \times m \times (T_f - T_i)$$
In this equation, C represents the specific heat of water, m represents the mass of the water, and T_f is the final temperature and T_i is the initial temperature of the water. Calculate the value of Q and record it in Table 1.

14. Assume that all the heat from the metal was transferred to the water in the calorimeter. Thus, the heat lost by the metal is equal to the heat gained by the water. Enter the value of the heat lost by the metal in Table 1. Remember to record a heat loss as a negative value.

15. Calculate the change in temperature of the metal.

16. The specific heat of a substance can be calculated by the following equation.
$$C = \frac{Q}{m(T_f - T_i)}$$
In this equation, Q represents the amount of heat gained or lost, m represents the mass of the substance, and $(T_f - T_i)$ represents the change in temperature of the substance. Calculate the specific heat of the metal. Record this value in Table 1.

17. Use the values of specific heats in Table 2 to identify the sample. Record the letter of the sample and name of the metal in the Data and Observations section.

Copyright © Glencoe/McGraw-Hill, a division of the McGraw-Hill Companies, Inc.

Laboratory Activity 1 (continued)

Data and Observations

Mass of calorimeter: _____ g

Mass of calorimeter and water: _____ g

Temperature of cool water: _____ °C

Temperature of metal: _____ °C

Temperature of water-metal mixture: _____ °C

Table 1

Metal	Specific heat (J/kg·C°)

Table 2

Measurement/Calculation	Material	
	Water	Metal
Mass (kg)		
Temperature change (°C)		
Specific heat (J/kg · °C)		
Heat gained or heat lost (J)		

Sample _____; Name of metal: _____

Questions and Conclusions

1. How well were you able to identify the metal using its specific heat?

_____

_____

2. In this experiment, the masses of the metal and the hot water were almost equal. However, the temperature decrease of the metal was much greater than the temperature rise of the water even though they had equal masses. Why?

_____

_____

Laboratory Activity 1 (continued)

3. In step 11 of the procedure, you recorded the temperature of the water bath as the temperature of the metal in it. Explain why you could do this.

_____

_____

_____

_____

_____

4. Could you improve your calorimeter by using two metal cans and aluminum foil in place of the two plastic cups and lids? Explain.

_____

_____

_____

_____

_____

Strategy Check

_____ Can you find the specific heat of a metal?

_____ Can you identify a metal when given its specific heat?

Thermal Energy from Foods

Chapter 6

You use food as fuel for your body. Food contains the stored energy you need to be active, both mentally and physically. Too keep your body processes going, your body must release the energy stored in food by digesting the food.

You cannot directly measure the energy contained in food. However, you can determine the amount of thermal energy released as a sample of food is burned by determining the thermal energy absorbed by water heated by the burning sample. By measuring the temperature change of a given mass of water, you can calculate the energy released from the food sample. Raising the temperature of 1 kg of water by 1 Celsius degree requires 4,190 joules of energy. This information can be expressed as the specific heat (C) of water, which is 4,190J/kg • °C. You can use the following equation to determine the heat (Q) released when a food sample is burned.

energy released = energy absorbed
energy absorbed = temperature change of
water × mass of water × specific heat of water

$$Q = (T_f - T_i) \times m \times C$$

Strategy
You will calculate a change in thermal energy.
You will account for the difference between energy released and energy absorbed.

Materials
large paper clip or long pin
food sample
aluminum potpie pan
metric balance
100-mL graduated cylinder

water
100-mL flask
utility clamp
ring stand

thermometer
wood splint
matches
watch or clock

Procedure

1. Wear a laboratory apron and safety goggles throughout this experiment. Straighten the paper clip and insert it through the food sample. Position the paper clip on the edges of the aluminum potpie pan as shown in Figure 1. Use the balance to determine the mass of the pan, paper clip, and food sample. Record the mass in Table 1 as m_1.

Figure 1

2. Use the graduated cylinder to add 50 mL of water to the flask. Clamp the flask on the ring stand about 5 cm above the tabletop. Use the thermometer to measure the temperature of the water. Record this value in Table 1 as T_i.

3. Ignite the wood splint with a match. **CAUTION:** *Always use care with fire.* Use the burning splint to ignite the food sample. Once the food sample is burning, safely extinguish the splint. Position the aluminum pan under the flask. The water in the flask should absorb most of the energy released by the burning food.

Laboratory Activity 2 (continued)

4. Stir the water with the thermometer and closely observe the temperature rise.
5. Blow out the flame of the burning food after about 2 minutes. Record the highest temperature of the water during the 2 minutes in Table 1 as T_f.
6. Allow the aluminum pan and its contents to cool. Determine the mass of the pan and contents after the release of energy. Record this value in Table 1 as m_2.

Figure 2

Burning food sample

Data and Observations

Table 1

Food sample	Mass (kg)		Temperature (°C)	
	m_1	m_2	T_i	T_f

$T_f - T_i =$ _____

m (mass of 50 mL of water) = _____

$(m_2 - m_1) =$ _____

$Q =$ _____

Heat absorbed per gram of food burned = _____

1. Calculate the rise in the water temperature by subtracting T_i from T_f. Record this value.
2. Use the equation given in the introduction to calculate the energy absorbed by the water when the food sample was burned. Be sure to use the mass of the water for m. Record this value.
3. Calculate the heat absorbed per gram of food by dividing the energy absorbed by the water by the mass of food burned $(m_2 - m_1)$. Record this value.
4. Your teacher will make a data table of food samples and energy absorbed by the water in the flask. Record your data in this table.

Laboratory Activity 2 (continued)

Questions and Conclusions

1. In order to calculate the amount of energy released or absorbed by a substance, what information do you need?

   _____

   _____

2. How do you know that energy was transferred in this experiment?

   _____

3. Did you measure the energy released by the food sample or the energy gained by the water?

   _____

   _____

4. Most of the energy of the burning food was absorbed by the water. What do you think happened to the small amount of energy that was not absorbed by the water?

   _____

   _____

5. Look at the data table of different food samples tested by your class. Which food sample released the most energy? Which food sample released the least energy?

   _____

   _____

6. Suppose 20.0g of your food sample is burned completely. Use a proportion to calculate the value of energy released.

   _____

   _____

Strategy Check

_____ Can you calculate a change in thermal energy?

_____ Can you determine whether energy is released or absorbed?

Wet Cell Battery

A car battery consists of a series of wet cells. Each wet cell contains two plates called electrodes, made of different metals or metallic compounds, and a solution called an electrolyte. Chemical reactions occur between the electrodes and the electrolyte. These reactions create a voltage difference between the two electrodes. Voltage difference is measured in a unit called the volt (V). If the two electrodes of a wet cell are connected by a conductor, electrons will flow through the conductor from one electrode, called the negative (−) electrode, to the other, called the positive (+) electrode. Within the cell, electrons will flow from the positive electrode to the negative electrode. The flow of electrons is caused by a chemical reaction.

Wet cells vary in their voltage difference. The voltage difference of a wet cell depends on the materials that make up the electrodes.

Strategy

You will construct a wet cell.
You will measure the voltage difference of a wet cell with a voltmeter.
You will observe how the voltage difference of a cell depends on the electrode materials.

Materials

2 alligator clips
250-mL beaker
long iron nail
100-mL graduated cylinder

paper towels
2 wires
tin strip
zinc strip

short wire tie
hydrochloric acid (HCI)
2 glass rods
voltmeter

Procedure

1. Place two glass rods across the top of the beaker.
2. Use an alligator clip to hang the zinc strip from one of the glass rods. The strip should hang near one side of the beaker.
3. Attach one wire to the alligator clip.

Attach the other end of the wire to the negative (−) terminal of the voltmeter.

4. Attach the iron nail to the second glass rod with the small wire tie. Attach the second alligator clip to the top of the nail. See Figure 1.
5. Connect the second alligator clip to the positive (+) terminal of the voltmeter with the other wire as shown in Figure 2.

Figure 1

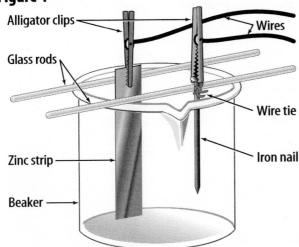

Figure 2

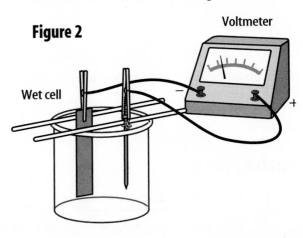

Laboratory Activity 1 (continued)

6. Carefully add 75 mL of hydrochloric acid to the beaker. **CAUTION:** *Hydrochloric acid causes burns. Rinse any spills immediately with water.* Make sure that the zinc strip and the nail are partially submerged in the acid.

7. Observe the wet cell. Record any changes in **Table 1**. Record the reading of the voltmeter in the data table.

8. Disconnect the wires. Carefully empty the acid from the beaker where your teacher indicates. Rinse the beaker, zinc strip, and iron nail and dry them with paper towels.

9. Repeat steps 1 through 8 using the zinc strip and the tin strip. In step 4, attach the tin strip to the glass rod with the alligator clip. After adding the HCl to the cell, record your observations and the reading of the voltmeter in Table 1.

Data and Observations

Table 1

Electrodes	Observations	Voltage difference (V)
zinc, iron		
zinc, tin		

Questions and Conclusions

1. How do you know that a chemical reaction has occurred in the wet cell after you added the acid?

   _____

2. Which pair of electrodes produced the greater voltage difference?

   _____

3. If one of the alligator clips is removed from the electrode, would a current exist? Explain.

   _____

   _____

4. Explain the difference between an electric current and voltage.

   _____

   _____

Strategy Check

_____ Can you construct a wet cell?

_____ Can you measure the voltage difference of a wet cell?

LAB 2 Laboratory Activity

Simple Circuits

Can you imagine a world without electricity? It is hard to believe that electrical energy became commercially available in the early 1880s.

The appliances plugged into the wall outlets of a room are part of an electric circuit. The most simple type of electric circuit contains three elements:

- a source of electrical energy, such as a dry cell;
- a conductor such as copper wire, which conducts an electric current; and
- a device, such as a lamp, which converts electrical energy into other forms of energy.

Complex circuits may contain many elements. How the elements are arranged in a circuit determines the amount of current in each part of a circuit.

Strategy

You will construct a series circuit and a parallel circuit.
You will observe the characteristics of the elements in circuits.
You will compare and contrast the characteristics of elements in series and parallel circuits.

Materials

aluminum foil
20-cm × 20-cm cardboard sheet
2 LEDs (light-emitting diodes)
metric ruler

9-V dry cell battery
9-V mini-battery clip
500-Ω resistor

scissors
stapler and staples
transparent tape

Procedure

Part A—Constructing and Observing a Series Circuit

1. Place the cardboard sheet on a flat surface.
2. Cut 2 1-cm × 10-cm strips of aluminum foil with the scissors.
3. Attach the battery clip to the 9-V mini-battery. Securely attach the battery and the two aluminum foil strips to the board with tape as shown in Figure 1.

4. Staple the exposed end of the red lead wire from the battery clip to the top foil strip. Staple the exposed end of the black lead wire from the clip to the bottom foil strip as shown in Figure 2. Be sure that the staples are pressing the exposed ends of the wires securely against the foil strips.

Figure 1

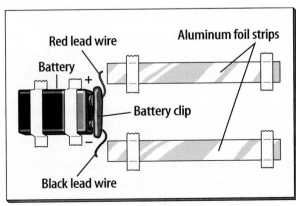

Figure 2

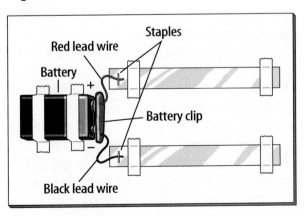

Laboratory Activity 2 (continued)

5. Cut a 1.0-cm-wide gap in the top foil strip with the scissors. Tape down the ends as shown in Figure 3.

6. Place the 500-Ω resistor across the gap. Securely staple the two wires of the resistor to the cut aluminum strip as shown in Figure 3.

Figure 3

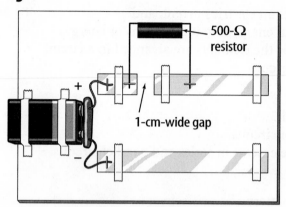

7. Push the long lead wire of the LED into the top aluminum strip. Push the short lead wire from the LED into the bottom strip as shown in Figure 4.

Figure 4

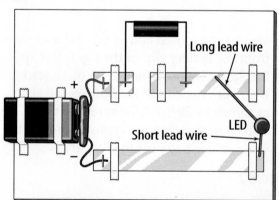

8. Observe the LED, noticing its brightness. Record your observation in the Data and Observations section.

9. Cut a 1-cm-wide gap in the lower foil strip with the scissors. Tape down the ends. Observe the LED. Record your observations in the Data and Observations section.

10. Insert the second LED across the gap in the bottom foil strip. Connect the long lead wire of this LED to the right segment of the strip as shown in Figure 5.

Figure 5

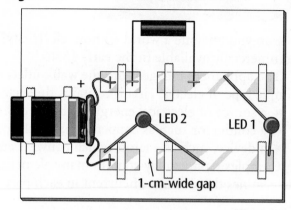

Attach the short lead wire to the left segment of the foil strip.

11. Observe both LEDs. Note if the brightness of LED 1 has changed from step 8. Record your observations in the Data and Observations section.

12. Predict what will happen to LED 2 if LED 1 is removed. Record your prediction.

13. Remove the first LED and observe the second LED. Record your observations.

14. Carefully remove LED 2, the staple from the black lead wire of the battery clip, and the two segments of the bottom foil strip from the cardboard sheet. (Disconnect LED 1 from the bottom foil strip first.) Leave all other circuit elements attached to the cardboard sheet for Part B of the experiment.

Part B—Constructing and Observing a Parallel Circuit

1. Cut a 1-cm × 10-cm strip of aluminum foil. Tape it to the board in place of the strip you removed in Step 14 of Part A. Staple the black lead wire of the battery clip to the lower foil strip.

2. Attach the first LED as you did in Step 7 of Part A. The long lead wire should still be attached to the top foil strip. Push the short lead wire through the bottom foil strip. Attach the second LED as shown in Figure 6 in the same manner.

3. Observe both LEDs. Note their brightness. Record your observations in the Data and Observations section.

Laboratory Activity 2 (continued)

4. Predict what will happen if LED 1 is removed. Record your prediction.
5. Remove LED 1. Record your observations.
6. Replace LED 2 and observe both LEDs. Note any change in brightness of the LEDs. Record your observations.
7. Predict what will happen if LED 2 is removed. Record your prediction.
8. Remove LED 2 and observe LED 1. Record your observations.

Figure 6

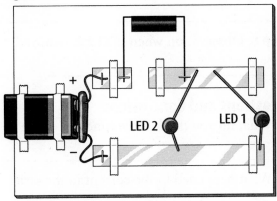

Data and Observations

Because the brightness of an LED in a circuit is directly related to the current in the circuit, the brightness of the LED is a measure of the current in that part of the circuit containing the LED.

Part A—Constructing and Observing a Series Circuit

Step 8. Observation of the LED when inserted into the foil strips:

_____

Step 9. Observation of the LED when lower foil strip is cut:

_____

Step 10. Observation of LEDs 1and 2 when LED 2 is inserted across gap in bottom foil strip:

_____

Step 11. Prediction if LED 1 is removed:

_____

Step 12. Observation when LED 1 is removed:

_____

Part B—Constructing and Observing a Series Circuit

Step 3. Observation of LEDs 1 and 2:

_____

Step 4. Prediction if LED 1 is removed:

_____

Step 5. Observation when LED 1is removed:

_____

Step 6. Observation when LED 2 is replaced:

_____

Laboratory Activity 2 (continued)

Step 7. Prediction if LED 2 is removed:

_____

Step 8. Observation when LED 2 is removed:

_____

_____

Questions and Conclusions

1. What do you think is the function of the 500-Ω resistor?

_____

2. What happened to the current in the series circuit when an LED was removed?

_____

3. What happened to the current in the series circuit when another LED was added?

_____

4. What happened to the current in the parallel circuit when an LED was removed?

_____

5. What happened to the current in the first LED in your parallel circuit when the second LED was added?

_____

6. Explain what your answer to question 4 indicates about the total amount of current in the resistor.

_____

7. How do you know if the lamps plugged into wall outlets in your house are part of a series circuit or a parallel circuit?

_____

_____

_____

Strategy Check

_____ Can you construct a series circuit?

_____ Did your observations reflect your predictions?

 **Laboratory Activity**

Comparing Magnetic Fields

A magnetic material is made of small regions called magnetic domains. These magnetic domains can be pictured as small bar magnets. When the domains are aligned, as shown in Figure 1, the magnetic fields of the domain add together. This causes the material to be surrounded by a magnetic field.

The magnetic field surrounding a magnet exerts a magnetic force on other magnets and magnetic materials. The direction of the magnetic field around a magnet can be represented by magnetic field lines. Magnetic field lines always begin on the north pole of a magnet and end on the south pole. Magnetic field lines are closer together where the magnetic field is stronger, and farther apart where the field is weaker.

Figure 1

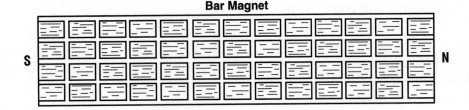

Bar Magnet

S   N

Strategy

You will observe the effect of a magnetic field around a magnet.

You will represent the shape of magnetic field lines by drawing an example.

You will compare and contrast the magnetic field lines around a bar magnet and a horseshoe magnet.

You will observe the interaction of two magnetic fields.

Materials

sheet of clear plastic
cardboard frame
masking tape
short bar magnets (2)
iron filings in a plastic container with a shaker top
small horseshoe magnet

Procedure

Part A—Magnetic Field of a Magnet

1. Attach the plastic sheet to the cardboard frame with masking tape.
2. Lay one bar magnet on a flat surface with its north pole at the left. Place the frame over the magnet so that the magnet is centered within the frame as shown in Figure 2.

Figure 2

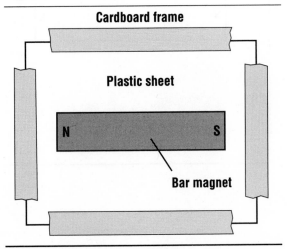

Cardboard frame

Plastic sheet

N   S

Bar magnet

Copyright © Glencoe/McGraw-Hill, a division of the McGraw-Hill Companies, Inc.

Laboratory Activity 1 (continued)

3. Gently sprinkle iron filings onto the plastic sheet. Observe how the magnetic field of the magnet affects the iron filings. The iron filings line up along the magnetic field lines around the bar magnet.

4. Sketch the magnetic field lines around the bar magnet in Figure 3 in the Data and Observations section.

5. Remove the lid from the container of the iron filings. Remove the tape holding the plastic sheet to the frame. Carefully lift the sheet and pour the iron filings into the container. Pick up any spilled filings with the other bar magnet and return them to the container. Replace the lid on the container.

6. Repeat steps 1 through 5 with the horseshoe magnet. Use Figure 4 in the Data and Observations section to sketch the magnetic field lines around the horseshoe magnet.

Part B—Interaction of Magnetic Fields

1. Attach the plastic sheet to the cardboard frame with masking tape.

2. Lay two bar magnets end to end on a flat surface as shown in Figure 5 in the Data and Observations section. Place the frame over the magnets so that they are centered within the frame.

3. Gently sprinkle iron filings onto the plastic sheet.

4. Sketch the magnetic field lines around the two bar magnets in Figure 5 in the Data and Observations section.

5. Remove the plastic sheet and return the iron filings to the container as before.

6. Repeat steps 1 through 5 for each position of the magnets shown in Figure 6 through Figure 8 in the Data and Observations section.

Data and Observations

Part A—Magnetic Field of a Magnet

Figure 3

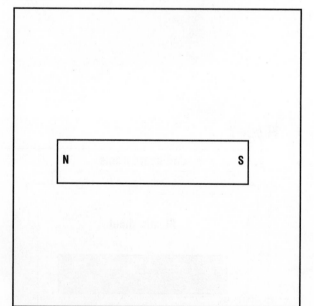

Figure 4

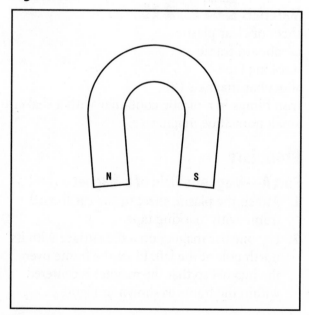

Laboratory Activity 1 (continued)

Part B—Interaction of Magnetic Fields

Figure 5

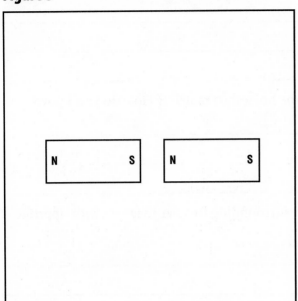

Figure 6

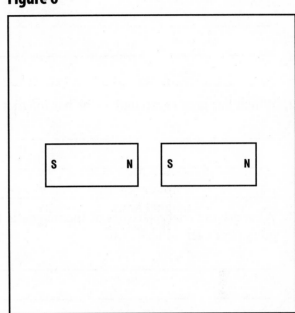

Figure 7

Figure 8

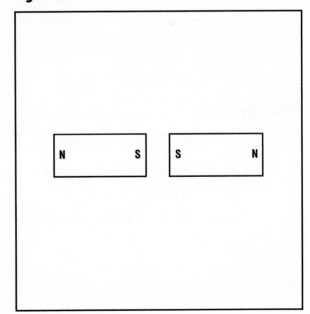

Laboratory Activity 1 (continued)

Questions and Conclusions

1. Why were you able to see the magnetic field lines using iron filings?

_____

_____

_____

2. Which has greater strength—the bar magnet or the horseshoe magnet? How do you know?

_____

_____

_____

3. What are the characteristics of the magnetic field surrounding two bar magnets with opposite poles near each other?

_____

_____

_____

4. What are the characteristics of the magnetic field surrounding two bar magnets with like poles near each other?

_____

_____

_____

_____

Strategy Check

_____ Can you see the effect of a magnetic field around a magnet?

_____ Can you compare and contrast the magnetic field lines around a bar magnet and a horseshoe magnet?

_____ Can you observe the interaction of two magnetic fields?

Creating Electromagnets

LAB 2 Laboratory Activity

A magnetic field exists around any wire that carries an electric current. By coiling the wire around a bolt or nail, the strength of the magnetic field will increase. A coil of wire wrapped around a bolt or nail will become an electromagnet if the wire is connected to a battery or other source of current. The magnetic force exerted by an electromagnet can be controlled by changing the electric current.

Strategy

You will construct several electromagnets.
You will compare the strength of the magnetic force of four electromagnets.
You will determine the relationship between the strength of the magnetic force and the number of turns of wire in the coil of the electromagnet.

Materials

iron bolts, identical, at least 5 cm long (4)
marking pen
masking tape
BBs, iron
*paper clips
small, plastic cups (2)
insulated wire
1.5-V dry cell battery
*Alternate materials

Procedure

1. Place masking tape on the heads of the bolts and label the bolts *A, B, C,* and *D.*
2. Put all the BBs in one cup.
3. Test each bolt for magnetic properties by attempting to pick up some of the BBs from the cup. Record your observations in the Data and Observations section.
4. Wrap 10 full turns of wire around bolt A. Wrap 20 turns of wire around bolt B, 30 turns around bolt C, and 40 turns around bolt D.

5. Use masking tape to connect the ends of the wires of bolt A to the dry cell as shown in the figure. Carefully use your electromagnet to pick up as many BBs as possible. Hold the electromagnet with the BBs over the empty cup and disconnect the wire to the dry cell. Make sure all the BBs fall into the cup. Count the number of BBs in the cup. Record this value in the table in the Data and Observations section.

Figure 1

BBs

Dry cell

Bolt

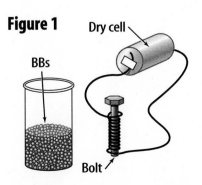

Laboratory Activity 2 (continued)

6. Return all the BBs to the first cup.
7. Repeat steps 5 and 6 using bolts B, C, and D. Record in the table the number of BBs each electromagnet picked up.
8. Use the blank graph in the Data and Observations section to construct a graph relating the number of BBs picked up by the electromagnet and the number of turns of wire in the electromagnet.

Determine which axis should be labeled *Number of BBs picked up* and which should be labeled *Number of turns of wire*. Plot your findings on the graph.

Data and Observations

Observation of the magnetic properties of the bolts alone:

_____

_____

_____

Electromagnet	Number of turns of wire	Number of BBs picked up
A	10	
B	20	
C	30	
D	40	

Laboratory Activity 2 (continued)

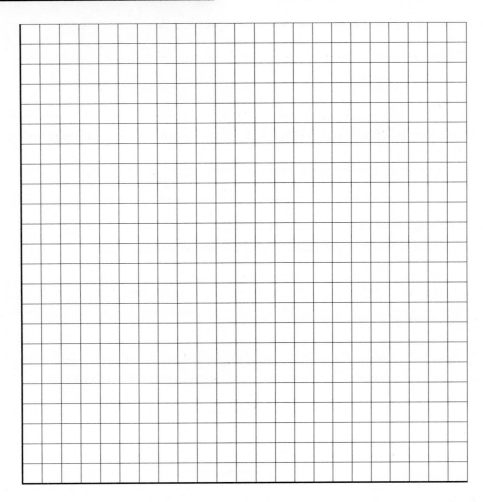

Questions and Conclusions

1. How is the number of BBs that were picked related to the magnetic force?

_____

_____

_____

2. How is the strength of the magnetic force exerted by an electromagnet related to the number of turns of wire?

_____

_____

_____

Laboratory Activity 2 (continued)

3. Explain how your graph supports your answer to question 2.

_____

_____

_____

4. Use your graph to predict how many BBs a bolt wrapped with 50 turns of wire will pick up.

_____

_____

_____

5. Why is it important that the bolts used in this experiment are identical?

_____

_____

_____

6. A magnetic force exists around a single loop of wire carrying an electric current. Explain why coiling a wire around a piece of iron increases the strength of an electromagnet.

_____

_____

_____

Strategy Check

_____ Can you construct electromagnets of different strengths?

_____ Can you compare the strength of the magnetic force exerted by different electromagnets?

_____ Can you explain how the strength of the magnetic force is related to the number of turns of wire in the coil of an electromagnet?

LAB 1 Laboratory Activity

Solar Cells

The Sun's radiant energy drives the weather and water cycles of Earth. This energy is necessary to sustain life on Earth. It might also be powering your pocket calculator or providing the hot water for your next shower.

Many pocket calculators contain solar cells. A solar cell is a device that converts radiant energy into electrical energy. In a circuit, a solar cell can produce an electric current. In this experiment you will investigate the power output of solar cells.

Strategy

You will determine the power of output of a solar cell.

You will describe how the power output of a solar cell is related to the power rating of its energy source.

You will compare sunlight and artificial sources of radiant energy.

Materials

25-, 60-, 75-, and 100-W lightbulbs
10-cm lengths of insulated wire (4)
light socket and cord
utility clamp
ring stand
meterstick
masking tape
solar cell
DC voltmeter
DC ammeter
resistor switch

Procedure

Part A—Artificial Sources of Light

1. Place the 25-W lightbulb into the light socket.
2. Attach the utility clamp to the ring stand. Use the utility clamp to position the light socket so that the bulb is 50 cm above the desk top. **CAUTION:** *Tape the socket's electrical cord onto the desk top so that no one can trip over the cord or topple the ring stand.*
3. Place the solar cell parallel to the desk and directly beneath the bulb.
4. Connect the voltmeter, ammeter, switch, and solar cell with the insulated wires as shown in Figure 1.
5. Plug the socket cord into an electrical outlet. Darken the room.

Figure 1

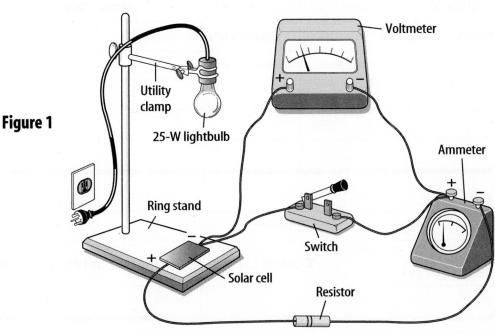

Utility clamp

25-W lightbulb

Voltmeter

Ammeter

Ring stand

Switch

Solar cell

Resistor

Laboratory Activity 1 (continued)

6. Switch on the 25-W bulb. Close the switch in the circuit. Measure the potential difference and the current with the voltmeter and ammeter, respectively. Record the value of the power rating of the bulb, the potential difference, and current in Table 1.

7. Open the circuit switch. Turn off the bulb and allow it to cool. **CAUTION:** *Lightbulbs generate heat. Do not touch the lightbulb for several minutes.*

8. Remove the lightbulb and replace it with the 60-W bulb.

9. Repeat steps 6–8 for the 60-W, 75-W, and 100-W lightbulbs.

Part B—Sunlight

1. Move the circuit containing the solar cell, voltmeter, ammeter, and switch to a sunny location, such as a window sill. Position the solar cell perpendicular to the sunlight.

2. Close the circuit switch. Measure the potential difference and the current with the voltmeter and ammeter, respectively. Record these values in Table 2. Open the switch.

Analysis

1. The power output (P) of the solar cell can be calculated using the following equation.
$$P = V \times I$$
In this equation V represents the potential difference measured in volts (V) and I represents the current measured in amperes (A). The unit of power is the watt (W). Use this equation to calculate the power output of the solar cell for each lightbulb. Record in Table 3 the value of the power rating of the lightbulb and the power output of the solar cell for each lightbulb.

2. Use Graph 1 to plot the power rating of the lightbulbs and the power output of the solar cell. Determine which variable should be represented by each axis.

3. Calculate the power output of the solar cell from Part B of the procedure. Record the value in Table 2.

4. Use Graph 1 to estimate the power rating of sunlight. Record the value in Table 2.

Data and Observations

Table 1

Lightbulb	Solar cell	
Power rating (W)	Potential difference (V)	Current (A)

Table 2

Solar cell			Sunlight
Potential difference (V)	Current (A)	Power output (W)	Power rating (W)

Laboratory Activity 1 (continued)

Table 3

Lightbulb	Solar cell
Power rating (W)	Power output (W)

Graph 1

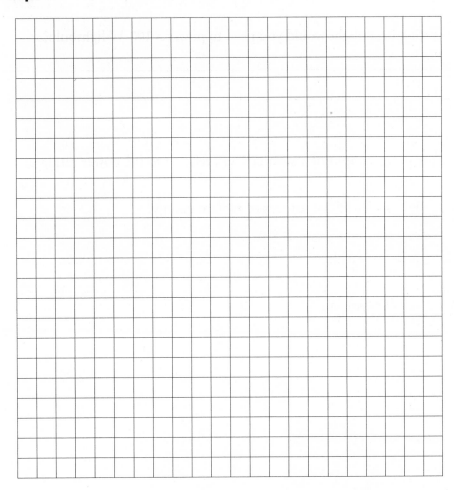

Laboratory Activity 1 (continued)

Questions and Conclusions

1. Which lightbulb produced the greatest power output of the solar cell?

_____

2. How is the power output of the solar cell related to the power rating of the lightbulbs?

_____

_____

_____

3. How does sunlight compare to artificial sources of light?

_____

_____

4. How many solar cells operating in sunlight would you need to power a 100-W lightbulb?

_____

_____

Strategy Check

_____ Can you determine the power output of a solar cell and relate it to the power rating of the energy source?

_____ Can you compare sunlight and artificial sources of radiant energy?

Using the Sun's Energy

LAB 2 Laboratory Activity

Chapter 9

You may recall how water in a garden hose lying in the grass can become hot on a sunny afternoon. Allowing the Sun's radiant energy to warm water in a solar collector is one way people are using solar energy to heat homes. To be useful and efficient, the solar collector must absorb and store a large amount of solar energy. In this experiment you will see how a solar collector can be used to heat water.

Strategy

You will build a solar hot water heater.
You will measure the temperature change of the heated water.
You will explain some benefits and problems in using solar heat.

Materials

100-mL graduated cylinder
water
plastic foam cup
pen or pencil
scissors
shallow box
metric ruler

black cloth or paper
tape
black rubber or plastic tubing, 5–6 m
buckets (2)
clothespin, spring-loaded
thermometer
graph paper

Procedure

Part A—Building a Solar Water Heater

1. Use the graduated cylinder to add 100 mL of water to the plastic foam cup. Use the pencil or pen to mark the surface of the water on the inside of the cup. (Do not use a felt tip marker.) Discard the water and save the cup for later use.

2. Make 2 holes near the bottom of a large shallow box as shown in Figure 1. The diameter of each hole should be the same as the diameter of the outside of the rubber tubing. Label one hole *IN* and the other *OUT*.

3. Line the box with a black cloth or paper. If paper is used, tape it securely in place. The top of the box must be open to the sun.

4. Fold the rubber tubing in place inside the box as shown. Arrange the tubing so most of it will be exposed to the sun. The ends of the tubing should extend from the holes in the box.

Figure 1

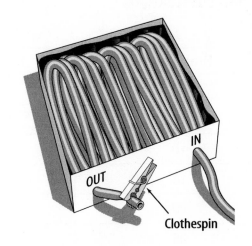

IN

OUT

Clothespin

Laboratory Activity 2 (continued)

Part B—Using Solar Energy

1. Move the box to a sunny location. Turn the box so that it is in direct sunlight.
2. Place an empty bucket beneath the tubing leading from the *OUT* hole. Place a second bucket filled to the top with water so it is above the level of the box. See Figure 2. Shade the bucket of water from the sun. Your teacher will show you how to start a siphon to fill the tube.
3. When the entire tube is filled with water, pinch the *OUT* tube with a spring-loaded clothespin. The flow of water should stop. Maintain the siphon. Do not remove the *IN* tube from the bucket of water.
4. Slowly release the clothespin and fill the plastic foam cup to the 100 mL line. New water should siphon into the system through the *IN* tube. Measure the temperature of the water in the cup with the thermometer. Record the temperature in Table 1 as the temperature at 0 minutes.

5. Collect samples of water from the water heater every 5 minutes. Check to make sure new water is siphoning into the system from the bucket. Measure and record the temperature of each water sample in Table 1.

Figure 2

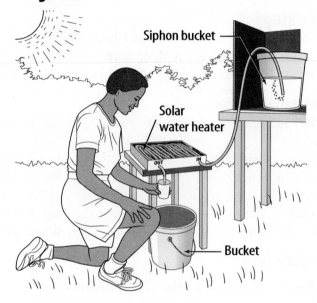

Siphon bucket

Solar water heater

Bucket

Data and Observations

Table 1

Time (min)	Temperature (°C)
0	
5	
10	
15	
20	
25	
30	

Laboratory Activity 2 (continued)

Use Graph 1 to graph the time and temperature of the water that you heated in the solar water heater. Determine which variable should be represented by each axis.

Graph 1

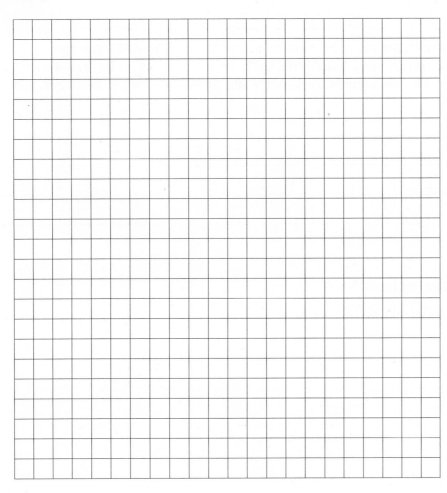

Questions and Conclusions

1. What happens to the temperature of the water in the tubing as it is exposed to the Sun?

_____

_____

_____

2. Explain how your graph indicates that solar energy can be used to heat water.

_____

_____

_____

Laboratory Activity 2 (continued)

3. Why is the inside of the box of the solar water heater black?

_____

_____

_____

4. Designers are using solar-heated water to heat entire houses. Tubes of heated water run through the walls of these solar houses. Usually the water heater is placed on the top of the house in a sunny location. Discuss some of the benefits and problems of using solar energy in this way to heat a house.

_____

_____

_____

_____

Strategy Check

_____ Can you build a solar hot water heater?

_____ Can you evaluate the usefulness of solar heat?

Velocity of a Wave

Laboratory Activity

Energy can move as waves through material such as ropes, springs, air, and water. Waves that need a material to pass through are called mechanical waves. Ripples in flags and sound waves are examples of mechanical waves. Electromagnetic waves, such as light, can be transmitted through matter as well as empty spaces.

The high part or hill of a transverse wave is the crest. The low part or valley of a transverse wave is the trough. The amplitude of a mechanical wave is the distance the material through which the wave is passing rises or falls below its usual rest position. Mechanical waves of large amplitude transmit more energy than mechanical waves of small amplitude.

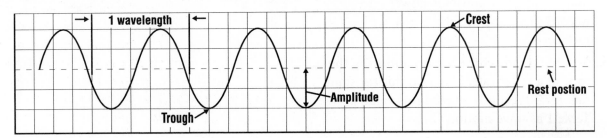

The wavelength is the distance between two similar points on successive waves. The number of wavelengths that pass a fixed point in one second is the frequency of the wave. Frequency is measured in a unit called hertz (Hz). A frequency of 1 Hz indicates that one wavelength is passing a point each second. The frequency can be found using the following equation:

frequency = number of wavelengths/1 second

The velocity of a wave depends upon the material through which the wave passes. The velocity of a wave is equal to its wavelength times its frequency. A wave's velocity is expressed in the same units as any measurement of velocity—meters per second (m/s).

velocity = wavelength × frequency

Strategy

You will identify the crest, trough, and amplitude of a wave.

You will determine the wavelength and frequency of a wave.

You will calculate the velocity of a wave.

Materials 🥽

instant developing camera
meterstick
20 pieces of colored yarn
rope, about 5 m long
   or
coiled spring toy

Procedure

Part A—Frequency of a Wave

1. Safety goggles should be worn throughout the experiment. Tie the pieces of yarn to the rope at 0.5 m intervals. Use the meterstick to measure the distances.

2. Tie one end of the rope to an immovable object, such as a table leg. Pull the rope so it does not sag.

3. Make waves in the rope by moving the free end up and down. Continue to move the rope at a steady rate. Observe the crests, troughs, and amplitude of the waves.

Laboratory Activity 1 (continued)

4. Continue making waves by moving the rope at a constant rate. Observe a particular piece of yarn. Count the number of wavelengths that you produce during a period of 30 seconds. Record this value in Table 1 as wave motion A.

5. Slow the rate at which you are moving the rope. Predict what will happen to the frequency. Count the number of wavelengths produced in 30 seconds while maintaining this constant slower rate. Record this value in Table 1 as wave motion B.

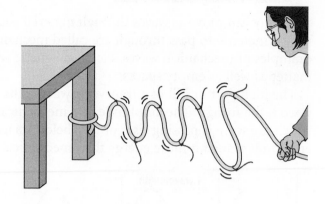

6. Repeat the procedure in step 4 moving the rope at a faster rate. Maintain this constant rate for 30 seconds. Record this value in Table 1 as wave motion C.

Part B—Velocity of a Wave

1. Using the same rope setup as in Part A, have a classmate move the rope with a constant motion. Record the number of wavelengths produced in 30 seconds in Table 2 as wave motion A. Photograph the entire length of the moving rope using the instant developing camera. Rest the camera on a table to keep it still.

2. Have your classmate increase the motion of the rope and take another photograph. Predict what will happen to the wavelength. Again count the number of wavelengths produced in 30 seconds, and record these values in Table 2 as wave motion B.

3. Observe the developed photographs. For each photograph, use the yarn markers to determine the length of one wavelength. Record these values in Table 2. You may tape the photographs to the last page of this Laboratory Activity.

4. Calculate the frequency of each of the three waves produced in Part A. Use the equation for the frequency found in the introduction. Record the values of the frequencies in Table 1.

5. Calculate the frequencies of the two waves produced in Part B. Record these values in Table 2.

6. Calculate the velocities of the two waves using the values of the wavelengths and frequencies in Table 2. Use the equation for velocity of a wave found in the introduction. Record the values of the velocities in Table 2.

Laboratory Activity 1 (continued)

Data and Observations

Part A—Frequency of a Wave

Wave motion	Number of waves in 30 s	Frequency (Hz)
A		
B		
C		

Part B—Velocity of a Wave

Wave motion	Number of waves in 30 s	Frequency (Hz)	Wavelength (m)	Velocity (m/s)
A				
B				

Questions and Conclusions

1. As you increased the motion of the rope, what happened to the frequency of the waves?

   _____

   _____

2. As the frequency of the waves increased, what happened to the wavelength?

   _____

   _____

3. As the frequency of the waves increased, what happened to the velocity of the waves?

   _____

   _____

4. Does your data indicate that the velocity of a wave is dependent or independent of its frequency? Explain.

   _____

   _____

   _____

Strategy Check

_____ Can you identify the crest, trough, and amplitude of a wave?

_____ Can you determine the wavelength and frequency of a wave?

_____ Can you calculate the velocity of a wave?

Laboratory Activity 1 (continued)

Attach photographs here.

Waves in Motion

Have you ever tossed a pebble into a puddle and watched the ripples? The ripples are actually small water waves. Have you wondered what affects those ripples? In this Lab Activity, you will look at ripples and how they behave.

Strategy

You will observe wave phenomena in a ripple tank.

Materials 🥽

ripple tank with light source and
    bottom screen
ripple bar
*3/4-in dowel, about 5 cm shorter than
    ripple tank*
paraffin block

dropper
glass plate, about 1/4 the area of the
    ripple tank
rubber stoppers cut to 1.5 cm high (2)
Alternate materials

Procedure

1. Turn on the light of the ripple tank. Allow the water to come to rest. Touch your finger once to the water surface to produce a wave. On the screen at the base of the tank, observe the shape of the wave. Does the speed of the wave seem to be the same in all directions? Record your observations in the table in the Data and Observations section.

2. Place the ripple bar in the water. Allow the water to come to rest. Using the flat of your hand to touch *only* the ripple bar, roll the ripple bar forward 1 cm. Observe the wave you produce. Record your observations in the table in the Data and Observations section. NOTE: Be careful to touch only the ripple bar when generating waves, do not touch the water with your hand.

3. Place a paraffin block in the tank parallel and closer to the deep end of the ripple tank. Orient the ripple bar to be parallel to the long edge of the paraffin block. Allow the water to come to rest. Use the flat of your hand to roll the ripple bar forward 1 cm, generating a wave that strikes the paraffin block barrier straight on. Observe what happens to the wave when it reaches the barrier. How does the wave move after it strikes the barrier? Record your observations in the Data and Observations section.

4. Reposition the paraffin block so that it is not aligned with the edges of the tank. This will change the angle at which the wave strikes it. Position the ripple bar so that it is parallel and closer to the shallow edge of the tank. After the water has come to a rest, move the ripple bar forward 1 cm with the flat of your hand. Observe the shape of the waves that reflect off the paraffin block. Record your observations. Remove the ripple bar from the water.

5. Allow the water to come to rest. Use the dropper to drop one drop of water onto the water surface. Observe the circular wave shape. Take note of how the wave reflects from the paraffin block and the point from which the reflected wave appears to originate. Record your observations in the Data and Observations section.

6. Place a paraffin barrier on one side of the tank, halfway between the shallow end and the deep end of the tank. Place the ripple bar parallel and closer to the shallow end. Again use a ripple bar to produce a straight wave. See step 3. Observe the part of the wave that strikes the barrier as well as the part that passes by it. Record your observations in the table.

Laboratory Activity 2 (continued)

7. Support a piece of glass with rubber stoppers so that the glass is in the shallow end of the tank 1.5 cm from the bottom of the tank and its top is just covered with water. Position the glass so that the edges of the glass are parallel to the edges of the tank. Place the ripple bar in the deep end of the tank, parallel to the edge. Allow the water to come to rest. Then move the ripple bar 1 cm to create a wave. Observe what happens as the waves pass from the

deep to the shallow end of the tank. Record your observations in the Data and Observations section.

8. Turn the glass so that its edges are no longer parallel to the edges of the ripple tank. Allow the water to come to rest, and then repeat step 7. Observe the shape of the waves that pass over the glass and that pass around the glass. Also note the speed of these waves. Record your observations.

Data and Observations

Step	Question	Observation
1	What is the shape of the wave?	1.
1	Is the speed of the wave the same in all directions?	2.
2	What is the shape of the wave?	3.
3	What happens to the wave at the barrier?	4.
3	What is the direction of the wave after it strikes the barrier?	5.
4	What is the shape of the reflected wave?	6.
5	How does the wave reflect from the paraffin block?	7.
5	From what point does the reflected wave appear to originate?	8.
6	What happens to the wave that hits the block?	9.
6	What happens to the wave that does not hit the block?	10.
7	What happens as waves pass from deep to shallow water?	11.
8	What is the shape of the wave that passes over the glass?	12.
8	What is the shape of the wave that does not pass over the glass?	13.
8	How do the speed of the two different waves compare?	14.

Laboratory Activity 2 (continued)

Questions and Conclusions

1. What is the shape of a wave produced at one point, such as with a drop of water or your fingertip?

   _____

2. What does a wave do when it hits a paraffin barrier?

   _____

3. Does a circular wave remain circular when it is reflected? Explain why this happens.

   _____

   _____

4. What happens to waves as they move into shallower water?

   _____

   _____

Strategy Check

_____ Can you identify behavior of waves?

Sound Waves and Pitch

Sounds are produced and transmitted by vibrating matter. You hear the buzz of a fly because its wings vibrate, the air vibrates, and your eardrum vibrates. The sound of a drum is produced when the drumhead vibrates up and down, the air vibrates, and your eardrum vibrates. Sound is a compressional wave. In a compressional wave, matter vibrates in the same direction as the wave travels. For you to hear a sound, a sound source must produce a compressional wave in matter, such as air. The air transmits the compressional wave to your eardrum, which vibrates in response to the compressional wave.

Compressional waves can be described by amplitude, wavelength, and frequency—the same as transverse waves. The pitch of a sound is related to the frequency of a compressional wave. You are familiar with high pitches and low pitches in music, but people are also able to hear a range of pitches beyond that of musical sounds. People can hear sounds with frequencies between 20 and 20,000 Hz.

Strategy

You will demonstrate that sound is produced by vibrations of matter.
You will vary the pitch of vibrating objects.

Materials

4 rubber bands of different widths but equal lengths
cardboard box, such as a shoe box or cigar box

Safety Precautions

Safety goggles should be worn throughout the experiment.

Procedure

1. Stretch the four rubber bands around a box as shown in Figure 1.

Figure 1

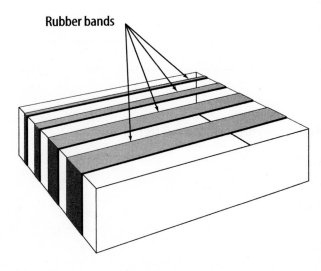

Rubber bands

2. Pluck the first rubber band, allowing it to vibrate. Listen to the pitch of the vibrating rubber band. Predict how the pitches of the other rubber bands will compare with this pitch. Record your prediction in the Data and Observations section. Pluck the remaining rubber bands. Record your observations about the variation in pitch.

3. Remove three rubber bands from the box. Hold the remaining rubber band tightly in the middle with one hand. Pluck it with the other. Move your hand up and down the rubber band to increase or decrease the length of the rubber band that can vibrate. Predict how the pitch will change as you change the length of the vibrating rubber band. Pluck the rubber band for each new length and record your observations of the length of the vibrating rubber band and pitch.

Laboratory Activity 1 (continued)

Data and Observations

1. Prediction of variation in pitch of sounds produced by rubber bands of different widths:

_____

_____

_____

2. Observation of changes in pitch with varying thickness of rubber bands:

_____

_____

_____

3. Observation of changes in pitch with varying length of the rubber band:

_____

_____

_____

_____

Questions and Conclusions

1. How does length affect the pitch of sound produced by a vibrating object?

_____

_____

2. How does the width of a rubber band affect its frequency of vibration?

_____

_____

3. Based on your results, how would you expect the pitch of sound produced by a vibrating string to be affected by the length of the string?

_____

_____

Strategy Check

_____ Can you demonstrate that sound is produced by vibrations of matter?

_____ Can you vary the pitch of vibrating objects?

LAB 2 Laboratory Activity

Musical Instruments

Musical instruments have been made and used for thousands of years by different cultures around the world. String, brass, woodwind, and percussion instruments all produce their own distinctive musical sounds. In this activity, you can make and compare the sounds made by several simple instruments.

Strategy

You will construct simple musical instruments.
You will compare and contrast the sounds made by these instruments.
You will classify the instruments according to their type.

Materials

block of wood, 15 cm × 10 cm × 5 cm
wire coat hanger
wire cutters
wire staples
hammer
6 beakers of the same size
wooden spoon
water
shoe box or tissue box
2 pieces of wood, 1 cm × 1 cm × 15 cm
5 rubber bands of varying lengths and
    thicknesses
6 nails of varying lengths, 5 cm to 20 cm

meterstick
string, 90 cm
scissors
metal spoon
2 plastic soda bottles with lids
dried peas, small pebbles, uncooked rice, or
    paper clips
plastic trash bag
string
tape
empty containers such as margarine tubs,
    plastic bowls, or cardboard tubes

Procedure

Part A—Twanger

1. Use wire cutters to cut a coat hanger into four or five pieces of different lengths. The lengths of the pieces should vary from 8 cm to 20 cm.
2. Use wire staples and a hammer to attach the lengths of wire to the wooden block, as shown in Figure 1.

Figure 1

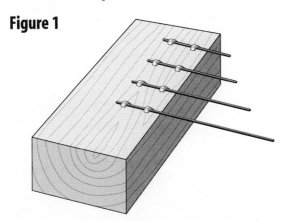

3. Pluck the wires with your thumb or a pen. In the data table in the Data and Observations section, describe the sounds and pitches produced by the various pieces of wire.

Part B—Xylophone

4. Set up six beakers of the same size in a row.
5. Leave the first beaker empty. Add increasing amounts of water to each of the remaining five beakers. The third beaker should be about half full and the last beaker should be almost full.
6. Tap the side of each beaker gently with a wooden spoon. Describe the sounds and pitches produced by each of the beakers.

Laboratory Activity 2 (continued)

Part C—Guitar

7. Stretch the rubber bands around the box lengthwise.
8. With a partner's help, slide one piece of wood under the rubber bands at one end of the box. Slide the other piece of wood under the rubber bands at the other end of the box. Your completed guitar should look like Figure 2.
9. Pluck the rubber bands with your fingers. Describe the sounds and pitches produced by each of the rubber bands.

Part D—Nail Chimes

10. Cut a piece of string into 15-cm pieces. Tie each piece of string around the meterstick, leaving a long end hanging down.
11. Tie the hanging end of each string around the head of a nail. Arrange the nails from shortest to longest.
12. Suspend the meterstick between two chairs or tables, as shown in Figure 3. Be sure the nails don't touch each other.
13. Use a metal spoon to tap the nails. Describe the sounds and pitches produced by each of the nails.

Figure 2

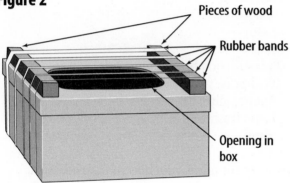

Pieces of wood

Rubber bands

Opening in box

Figure 3

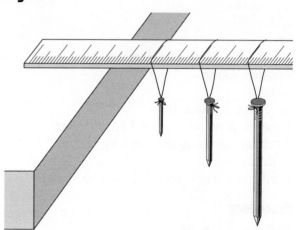

Laboratory Activity 2 (continued)

Part E—Shakers

14. Place a small amount of dried peas, small pebbles, uncooked rice, or paper clips into one plastic bottle. Screw the cap on the bottle.

15. Place a small amount of another material in a second plastic bottle and screw on the cap.

16. Shake each bottle or tap it against your hand. Describe the sounds made by each shaker.

Part F—Drums

17. Cut down the sides of the plastic bag to make one large sheet.

18. Place one of your containers open side down on the plastic sheet. Cut around the container, leaving about an extra 10 cm all around the container.

19. With a partner, stretch the plastic tightly over the top of the container. Use string and tape to hold the plastic in place, as shown in Figure 4.

20. Repeat steps 18 and 19 with a container of a different size.

21. Hit the top of your drums lightly with your fingers or a pencil. Describe the sounds made by each drum.

Figure 4

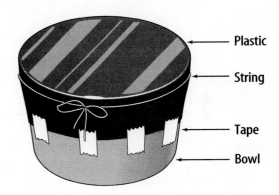

Plastic

String

Tape

Bowl

Laboratory Activity 2 (continued)

Data and Observations

Instrument	Sounds and pitches
Twanger	
Xylophone	
Guitar	
Nail chimes	
Shakers	
Drums	

Questions and Conclusions

1. Which instruments were able to produce sounds of different pitches?

   _____

2. What caused the different pitches of sounds in each of those instruments?

   _____

3. Classify each of the instruments you made by type.

   _____

   _____

4. How does the length of a piece of wire or a nail affect its frequency of vibration?

   _____

Strategy Check

_____ Can you construct simple musical instruments?

_____ Can you compare and contrast the sounds made by these instruments?

_____ Can you classify the instruments according to their type?

Observing the Electromagnetic Spectrum

Electromagnetic waves are produced by electric charges that move or vibrate back and forth. The frequency of the electromagnetic wave is the same as the frequency at which the charge vibrates. Except for their frequency and wavelength, all electromagnetic waves are the same and travel at the same speed, 300,000 km/s in a vacuum. The electromagnetic spectrum is used to classify electromagnetic waves according to their frequency and wavelength. Humans are only able to see visible light, which is one small portion of the spectrum. In this activity, you will create a model of the infrared, visible, and ultraviolet portions of the electromagnetic spectrum. The model you create will be made to scale based on wavelength.

Strategy

You will create a scale model of portions of the electromagnetic spectrum.
You will demonstrate that visible light makes up a very small portion of the electromagnetic spectrum.

Materials

calculator
meterstick or metric ruler (marked in millimeters)
scissors
one piece of paper in each of the following colors: red, orange, yellow, green, blue, violet, white, and black
black marker
cellophane tape
flashlight
prism

Procedure

1. The wavelengths for the visible, infrared, and ultraviolet portions of the spectrum are represented in meters in the data table. Complete a metric conversion calculation to find the length of the waves in nanometers. One nanometer is 1×10^{-9} of a meter.

   Use the following conversion factors to convert the wavelengths to nanometers:
   10^{-6} M = 1,000 nanometers;
   10^{-7} M = 100 nanometers; and
   10^{-8} M = 10 nanometers.

2. The scale that will be used to build the model of the spectrum is 1 nanometer equals 1 millimeter. Therefore, if a wavelength is x nanometers, the model for that wavelength should measure x millimeters. Record your calculations for scale wavelength in millimeters in the table in the Data and Observations section.

3. Work together as a class on the metric conversion calculation for red light. It is good to begin with red light rather than infrared, which is listed first in the data table, because the length of the scale model for infrared light is significantly longer than the scale models of any of the visible light colors.

4. Fill in the scale length in the millimeters column in your data table for red light. This column should always be the same as the final answer for wavelength in nanometers.

5. Use the colored paper to represent the different colors in the visible spectrum. Red paper will be used for the wavelength of red light, orange paper for orange light, and so on. White paper will represent infrared, and black paper will represent ultraviolet.

Laboratory Activity 1 (continued)

6. Cut a strip of red paper that is 2.5 cm wide and the same length as the number you have written in your column for scale length in millimeters.

7. Once you have a strip of red paper that is 750 mm (75 cm) long, mark the actual wavelength of red light, 7.5×10^{-7} m, on the strip.

8. Complete a metric conversion calculation and cut strips for each of the electromagnetic waves represented in the data table. When you have finished, you should have eight strips of paper of different lengths and colors in your model.

9. Align your strips horizontally, directly underneath each other, with the longest strip (which should be infrared) on top and the shortest strip (which should be ultraviolet) on the bottom. Tape all the strips together to make one large sheet.

10. Shine the flashlight through the prism in order to see the visible spectrum you have just modeled.

Data and Observations

Wave	Actual wavelength in meters	Calculation	Actual wavelength in nanometers	Scale wavelength in millimeters
1. Infrared	1×10^{-6}			
2. Red	7.5×10^{-7}			
3. Orange	6.25×10^{-7}			
4. Yellow	5.75×10^{-7}			
5. Green	5.25×10^{-7}			
6. Blue	4.5×10^{-7}			
7. Violet	4×10^{-7}			
8. Ultraviolet	3×10^{-8}			

Questions and Conclusions

1. What colors did you observe from the prism? List them in order from top to bottom.

_____

_____

2. Why do we use the scale of 1 nanometer equals 1 millimeter?

_____

_____

_____

Laboratory Activity 1 (continued)

3. How many times longer is the wavelength of the infrared wave than the wavelength of the ultraviolet wave?

_____

_____

_____

_____

4. A radio wave is approximately 3 meters long. If we were to make this wave part of our model, how long would the strip of paper representing the radio wave have to be?

_____

_____

5. Why didn't you include the whole electromagnetic spectrum in your model?

_____

_____

_____

_____

Strategy Check

_____ Can you compare the wavelength sizes of the electromagnetic spectrum?

_____ Can you demonstrate that visible light is a small portion of the electromagnetic spectrum?

LAB 2 Laboratory Activity

Catching the Wave

When you listen to your radio, you are hearing the information that is carried by electromagnetic waves. Many electronic and electrical devices produce low frequency electromagnetic waves. In this lab, you will detect these waves.

Strategy

You will detect electromagnetic waves.
You will determine what produces electromagnetic waves.

Materials

9-V battery
mini audio amplifier
telephone pickup coil
strong permanent magnet
string
variety of appliances: calculators, watches, radios, computers, lights, burning candles, vacuum cleaners

Procedure

1. Put the 9-V battery into the amplifier and plug in the telephone pickup coil.
2. Place the strong permanent magnet on the table. Slowly bring the pickup coil near the magnet.
3. Hold the pickup coil still. Attach the magnet to a string so that it hangs just above the coil and allow it to swing.

Listen for the electromagnetic waves. Record your observations in the table in the Data and Observations section.

4. Use the pickup coil to try to pick up signals from televisions, computers, lights, burning candles, appliances, watches, etc. Record your observations.

Data and Observations

Appliance	Sound
Pickup coil and amplifier	

Laboratory Activity 2 (continued)

Questions and Conclusions

1. What causes sound waves?

_____

_____

_____

_____

_____

2. Does the sound change when two items are close to the coil?

_____

_____

_____

_____

_____

3. Why can you hear the electromagnetic waves from some objects that are not electrical appliances?

_____

_____

_____

_____

_____

4. How can you predict which objects will produce an electromagnetic wave and which will not?

_____

_____

_____

_____

_____

Laboratory Activity 2 (continued)

5. Some people think that electromagnetic waves are harmful to our health. Do you think we could get rid of these waves?

_____

_____

_____

_____

_____

Strategy Check

_____ Can you detect electromagnetic waves?

_____ Can you predict if an item will produce electromagnetic waves?

Producing a Spectrum

Each color of light has a particular wavelength. The colors that make up white light can be separated into individual colored bands called a spectrum. A spectrum can be produced by refraction or interference.

When light passes from one substance into another, its speed changes. If a ray of light passes from one substance into another at an angle, its direction also changes. The change in speed and possible change in direction of light as it enters a substance is called refraction. Refraction of light can be seen with a prism. As light enters a prism, each wavelength is bent a different amount. Thus, the wavelengths are separated into a spectrum.

When you see colors in soap bubbles or in drops of oil on wet pavements, you are observing the interference of light rays. Some of the light striking the outer surface of a thin film, such as a soap bubble, is reflected to your eyes. Some of the light passing through the bubble film is reflected from the inner surface of the film to your eyes. The rays from the inner surface travel a slightly longer path than the rays reflected from the outer surface. The waves do not arrive at your eyes together. They are out of phase. Your eyes may receive the crest of one wave along with the trough of another wave.

Waves out of phase cancel each other and no color is produced. Waves that are out of phase undergo destructive interference. Other areas of the thin film reflect light rays that are in phase, and you see bands of color. The colors you see are due to constructive interference. The interference of light reflecting from the other two surfaces of a thin film creates bands of different colors. These bands change position if the viewing angle changes or the film changes thickness.

Strategy

You will describe the spectrum made by a prism.

You will describe an interference pattern.

You will explain how a spectrum can be produced by refraction of light and by interference.

Materials 🥽 🧤 ✂️ 🤚

Part A
projector or other
   light source
prism
tape
white paper

Part B
bowl
water
index card
clear nail polish
scissors

Procedure

Part A—Refraction

1. Darken the room. Your teacher will set up a projector or other light source in the room. **CAUTION:** *Do not look directly into the light source.* Hold a prism in the beam of the projector so the light strikes one of the three rectangular sides. Rotate the prism by holding the triangular ends so a pattern of colors is produced on the wall. Tape a piece of white paper to the wall where the spectrum appears.

2. Observe the spectrum and the order of the colors. Write in the names of the colors, in the order you see them, on Figure 3 in the Data and Observations section.

Laboratory Activity 1 (continued)

Part B—Interference

1. Fill the bowl with water.
2. Cut two holes, each about 1 cm in diameter, in the index card.
3. Place two separate drops of nail polish on the surface of the water. The polish will harden to a film. Position one hole of the index card under one of the films of nail polish and carefully lift the film from the water. Repeat, using the second hole and the second film. Hold the card vertically and allow the films to dry in place.
4. Hold the index card away from the light, as shown in Figure 2. Look down at the films. If you change the position of your head while viewing the card, you should observe a spectrum on each film.
5. Describe and make a drawing of the color patterns you observe in the Data and Observations section.

Figure 1

Nail polish film

Figure 2

Data and Observations

Part A

1. Label the colors of the spectrum you observed.

Figure 3

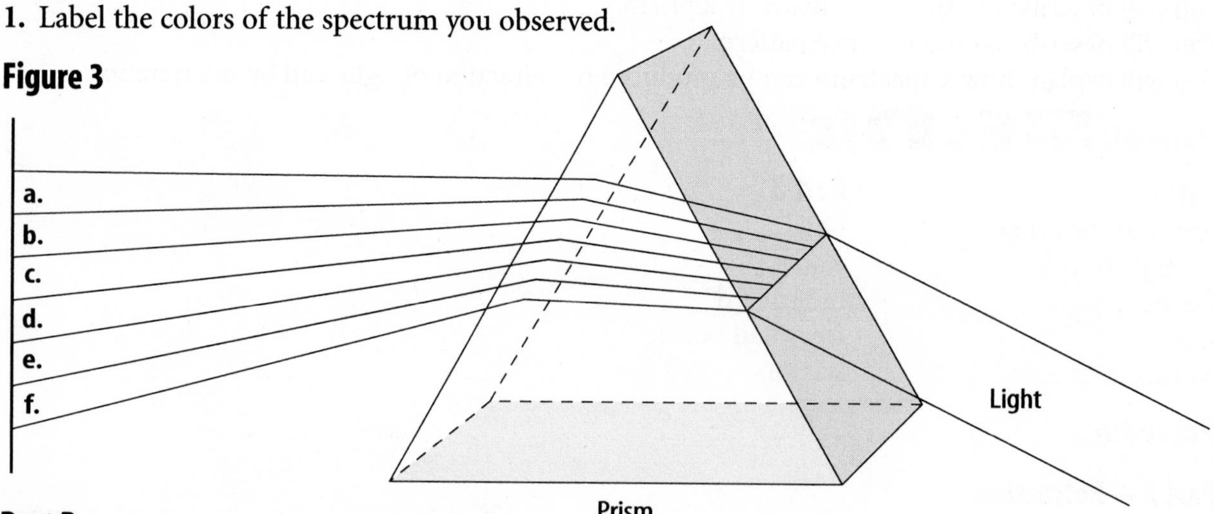

a. ____
b. ____
c. ____
d. ____
e. ____
f. ____

Light

Prism

Part B

1. Description of color patterns on thin film:

_____

_____

2. Drawing of the interference pattern on the thin film:

Laboratory Activity 1 (continued)

Questions and Conclusions

1. What is refraction of light?

_____

_____

2. What is destructive interference? What is constructive interference?

_____

_____

3. Label the surfaces of the cross-sectional diagram of the thin film shown in Figure 4. Show the two things that happen to a ray of light that strikes the outer surface. Show what happens to a ray of light that continues and strikes the inner surface. Label each instance of reflection and refraction that occurs when light strikes a thin film.

Figure 4

4. Compare and contrast the production of a spectrum from a prism and from a thin film.

_____

_____

_____

_____

Laboratory Activity 1 (continued)

5. Label each figure below as an example of reflection, refraction, or interference.

Figure 5

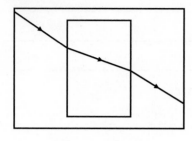 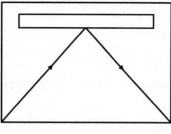 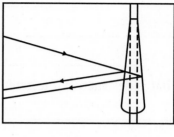

a. _____   b. _____   c. _____

Strategy Check

_____ Can you describe the spectrum made by a prism?

_____ Can you describe an interference pattern?

_____ Can you explain how a spectrum can be produced by refraction of light and by interference?

LAB 2
Laboratory Activity

Light Intensity

Chapter 13

Have you ever noticed how the brightness of the light from a flashlight changes as you move closer to or farther away from it? Likewise, have you ever noticed how the strength of the signals from a radio station fades on a car radio as you move away from the transmitting tower? Both light and radio signals are electromagnetic waves. These two examples seem to suggest that the intensity of energy and distance are related. What is the relationship between light intensity and distance? Is there also a relationship between light intensity and direction?

In this experiment you will use a photo resistor, a device that changes its resistance to an electric current according to the intensity of the light hitting it. The resistance is measured in a unit called an ohm (Ω). Photo resistors are often used in burglar alarm systems. A beam of light shines on the photo resistor. If anyone or anything passes through the beam, the intensity of the light is changed. Because the photo resistor is in an electric circuit, the current in the circuit changes and this causes an alarm to sound.

Strategy

You will measure the effect of distance on light intensity.
You will measure the effect of direction on light intensity.
You will interpret graphs relating light intensity, distance, and direction.

Materials

photo resistor
pencil
tape
ring stand
meterstick
black tape

multimeter or
    ohmmeter
25-W lightbulb
    and lamp socket
utility clamp
colored pencils

Procedure

1. In the Data and Observations section, write hypotheses explaining the relationships between light intensity and distance and between light intensity and direction.

2. Mount the photo resistor on a pencil with tape. See Figure 1.

3. Lay the meterstick on a flat, hard surface. Place small pieces of black tape at 0.10 m intervals along the meterstick.

4. Set the lightbulb and socket on a smooth, flat surface.

5. Clamp the meterstick to the ring stand with the utility clamp. Arrange the meterstick so that the lightbulb is at the 0.00 m marker. See Figure 2.

Figure 1

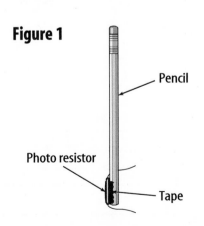

Pencil

Photo resistor

Tape

Figure 2

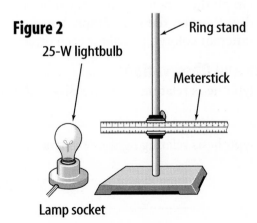

Ring stand

25-W lightbulb

Meterstick

Lamp socket

Laboratory Activity 2 (continued)

6. Attach the wires of the photo resistor to the multimeter or ohmmeter. If using a multimeter, set the meter to measure resistance and attach the wires to the appropriate terminals. Darken the room before any measurements are taken.

7. Turn off the bulb and place the photo resistor at the 1.00 m marker. See Figure 3.

8. Measure the resistance using the multimeter or ohmmeter. Record the value in Table 1 in the column marked *East*.

9. Move the photo resistor to the 0.90 m marker. Record the value in the same column of the data table.

10. Continue advancing the photo resistor to each marker. Record the meter reading at each position. The last reading should be taken at the 0.10 m marker.

11. Assume that the meterstick was oriented with the 1.0 m marker pointing to the East. Repeat the procedure for each of the three remaining directions shown in Figure 4.

12. Use Graph 1 to graph your data. Place the distance values on the *x*-axis and the resistance values on the *y*-axis. Label the *x*-axis. *Distance from light source (m)* and the *y*-axis *Resistance (Ω)*.

13. Graph the data for each of the other three directions on the same graph. Use a different colored pencil for each direction.

Figure 3

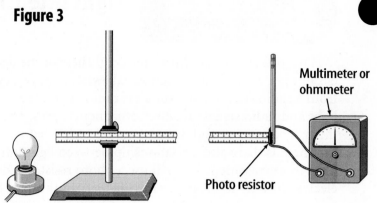

Multimeter or ohmmeter

Photo resistor

Figure 4

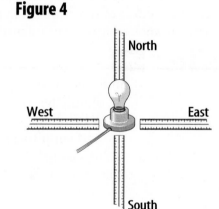

North

West

East

South

Data and Observations

1. Hypothesis relating light intensity and distance:

_____

2. Hypothesis relating light intensity and direction:

_____

_____

_____

Laboratory Activity 2 (continued)

Table 1

Distance (m)	Resistance (Ω)			
	East	West	North	South
1.00				
0.90				
0.80				
0.70				
0.60				
0.50				
0.40				
0.30				
0.20				
0.10				

Graph 1

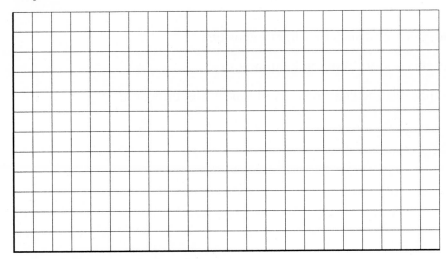

Questions and Conclusions

1. Look at the graph. Describe how the resistance and distance are related.

_____

_____

2. How are light intensity and distance related?

_____

Laboratory Activity 2 (continued)

3. What does the graph indicate about the relationship between intensity of light and direction?

_____

_____

_____

4. Why was it necessary to darken the room before doing this experiment?

_____

_____

5. Do the results of this experiment support your original hypotheses?

_____

6. Light from the Sun travels to Earth from a distance of almost 150 million km. If Earth were farther away from the Sun, what effects would be felt on Earth's surface? What effects would be felt if Earth were closer to the Sun?

_____

_____

_____

Strategy Check

_____ Can you measure the effects of distance on light intensity?

_____ Can you measure the effect of direction on light intensity?

_____ Can you interpret graphs relating light intensity, distance, and direction?

Reflection of Light

Light travels in straight lines. When a light ray strikes a smooth surface, such as polished metal or still water, it is reflected. The angle between the incoming ray, the incident ray, and the normal line is called the angle of incidence. The normal line is a line forming a right angle with the reflecting surface as shown in Figure 1. The angle between the reflected ray and the normal line is called the angle of reflection.

Rough or irregular surfaces reflect parallel light rays in all directions. Because light is reflected from rough surfaces in all directions, these surfaces cannot be used to produce sharp images.

Figure 1

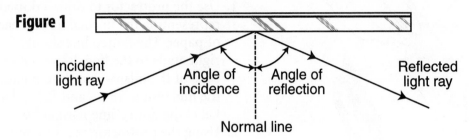

Strategy

You will observe that light travels in straight lines.

You will identify the angles of incidence and reflection of reflected light.

You will describe the relationship between the angle of incidence and the angle of reflection.

Materials

white paper (3 sheets)   book

flashlight or projector   plane mirror

masking tape   comb

pen or pencil   protractor

Procedure

1. Use masking tape to attach one sheet of white paper to the cover of the book. Tape the comb to the edge of the book. The teeth of the comb should extend above the edge of the book as shown in Figure 2.

2. Darken the room. Shine the flashlight through the comb onto the paper from as far away as possible. Support the flashlight on a table or books. Observe the rays of light on the paper. Record your observations in the Data and Observations section.

Figure 2

Teeth extend above edge of book.

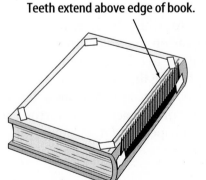

Laboratory Activity 1 (continued)

3. Stand the plane mirror at a right angle to the surface of the book cover. Position the mirror about two-thirds of the width of the book away from the comb. Adjust the mirror so that the light rays hit it at right angles. See Figure 3.

Figure 3

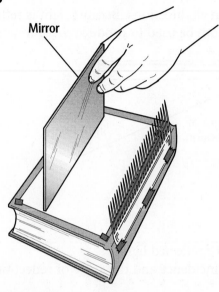

Mirror

4. Rotate the mirror so that the light rays strike it at various angles of incidence. As you turn the mirror, observe the reflected rays of light. Form a hypothesis relating the incident and reflected rays and write it in the Data and Observations section.

5. With the mirror turned so the incident rays strike it at an angle of about 30°, study a single incident ray. One partner should hold the mirror while the other traces the path of the ray on the white sheet of paper. Be careful not to change the angle of the mirror while tracing the ray. Label the incident ray *I* and the reflected ray *R*. Draw a line along the edge of the back of the mirror. Label the sheet of paper *Trial A*.

6. Repeat step 5 using a new sheet of paper on the book. Hold the mirror at a greater angle and trace the ray and the edge of the back of the mirror. Label this sheet *Trial B*. Repeat step 5 for a third time and label the sheet of paper *Trial C*.

7. After analyzing the ray tracings, attach them to page 11.

Analysis

1. Use the protractor to draw a dotted line representing the normal line on each sheet of paper. The dotted line should form a right angle to the line drawn along the back edge of the mirror and should pass through the junction of rays *I* and *R*. See Figure 4. Label the dotted line *normal line*.

2. Using the protractor, measure the angle between the normal line (dotted line) and the tracing of the incident ray (*I*) for Trial A. Record this value in Table 1. Measure the angle between the normal line and the tracing of the reflected ray (*R*), and record this value in the data table. Measure and record the angles for Trials B and C in the same way.

Figure 4

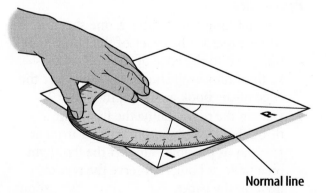

Normal line

Laboratory Activity 1 (continued)

Data and Observations

Observation of light rays in step 2 of the procedure:

_____

Hypothesis:

_____

_____

_____

Table 1

Trial	Angle of incidence	Angle of reflection
A		
B		
C		

Attach ray tracings here.

Laboratory Activity 1 (continued)

Questions and Conclusions

1. Explain how your observations of light passing between the teeth of a comb support the statement that light travels in straight lines.

_____

_____

_____

_____

2. Why did you mark the position of the *back* edge of the plane mirror on your ray tracings?

_____

_____

_____

_____

3. As you increased the angle of incidence, what happened to the angle of reflection?

_____

_____

4. Explain the relationship between the angle of incidence and the angle of reflection.

_____

_____

_____

_____

Strategy Check

_____ Can you identify the angles of incidence and reflection of reflected light?

_____ Can you explain the relationship between the angles of incidence and reflection?

Magnifying Power

Parallel rays of light passing through a convex lens are refracted toward a single point called the focal point. Rays passing through the center of the lens are not bent at all. Rays passing through the edges of the lens bend sharply. The distance between the focal point and the midpoint of the lens is the focal length. As you can see in Figure 1, the curvature of a lens determines the position of its focal point. A thin lens has only a slight curvature. It has a long focal length because the focal point is far from the lens. A thicker lens has a greater curvature. It has a shorter focal length because its focal point is closer to the center of the lens.

Figure 1

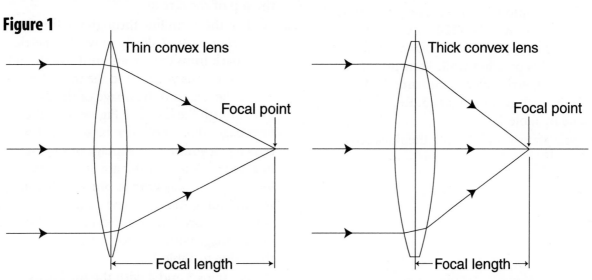

You have probably used a magnifying glass to make objects appear larger. A magnifying glass is a convex lens. The magnifying power of a convex lens indicates how many times larger the image is compared to the object. A lens with a magnifying power of 3× indicates that the image of a line 1 cm long will appear to be 3 cm long when viewed through the lens.

The magnifying power of a convex lens can be calculated if the focal length of the lens is known. How is the magnifying power of a lens related to its focal length?

Strategy
You will measure the focal length of two lenses.
You will predict the magnifying power of each lens.
You will determine the magnifying power of each lens.

Materials
book
large white index card
masking tape
thick convex lens
thin convex lens
metric ruler

Laboratory Activity 2 (continued)

Procedure

Part A—Measuring the Focal Length of a Convex Lens

1. Make a screen by taping the large white index card to a book as shown in Figure 2.
2. Using the thin lens, focus the light from a bright light source onto the screen. Direct sunlight is best, but a lamp can be used.
3. Adjust the lens so that a small pinpoint of light falls onto the screen. The pinpoint is the focal point. **CAUTION:** *Do not focus the light from the lens at anyone.* Hold the lens in this position while your partner uses the metric ruler to measure the focal length, as shown in Figure 3. Record this value in Table 1.
4. Repeat steps 2 and 3 using the thick lens.

Part B—Determining the Magnifying Power of a Lens

1. Use the metric ruler to draw a 2.0-cm horizontal line about 0.5 cm below the top of the screen.
2. Place the screen about 25 cm away.
3. Have your partner hold the metric ruler slightly behind and parallel to the screen. The bottom of the ruler should align with the top of the screen.
4. Look at the 2-cm line through the thin lens. Have your partner slowly move the metric ruler back from the screen until you do not have to refocus your eye to see the ruler above the lens and the image of the 2-cm line *through* the lens. See Figure 4 on the next page. When both can be seen without refocusing your eye, the image of the 2-cm line and the metric ruler are at the same location. You may have to practice this step several times. After you feel comfortable with this procedure, approximate the length of the image with the metric ruler. Record this value in Table 1.
5. Repeat steps 3 and 4 with the thick lens.

Figure 2

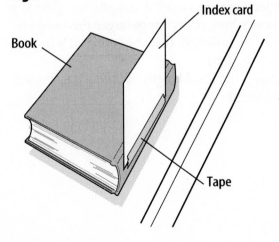

Index card

Book

Tape

Figure 3

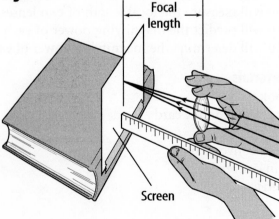

Focal length

Screen

Laboratory Activity 2 (continued)

Figure 3

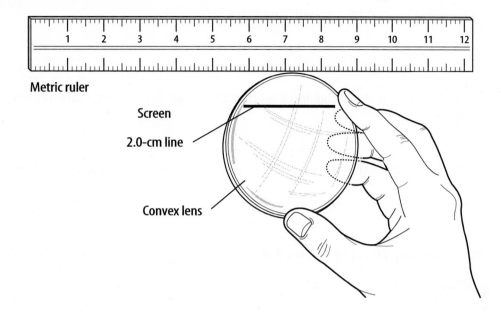

Metric ruler

Screen

2.0-cm line

Convex lens

Data and Observations

Table 1

Lens	Focal length (cm)	Length of image (cm)
thin		
thick		

Table 2

Lens	Magnifying power	
	Method 1	**Method 2**
thin		
thick		

1. Calculate the magnifying power of each lens by finding the ratio of the length of the image and the 2-cm line. Record these values under Method 1 in Table 2.

2. The magnifying power of a lens can also be calculated using the following equation.

$$magnifying\ power = \frac{focal\ length}{25\ cm - focal\ length}$$

Use this equation to calculate the magnifying factor of each lens. Record these values under Method 2 in Table 2.

Laboratory Activity 2 (continued)

Questions and Conclusions

1. Describe the image formed by a magnifying glass.

_____

_____

2. How does the location of the image indicate that the image formed by a magnifying glass is a virtual image?

_____

3. Which method of determining the magnifying power has less chance for error? Explain.

_____

_____

4. How is the magnifying power of a lens related to the curvature of the lens? To focal length?

_____

_____

5. Can a drop of water resting on a surface act as a magnifying glass? Explain.

_____

_____

_____

6. A student draws a 1-cm × 2-cm rectangle on a piece of paper. What will be the area of the image of the rectangle if the student observes the drawing through a 2× hand lens?

_____

Strategy Check

_____ Can you measure the focal length of a concave or convex lens?

_____ Can you determine the magnifying power of a lens?

Chromatography

Chromatography is a useful method for separating substances in a mixture. As you recall, the substances in a mixture are not chemically combined. Therefore, they can be separated. Chromatography can be used to separate the substances in certain mixtures because these substances dissolve at different rates.

Many mixtures, such as inks and food colorings, consist of two or more dyes. To separate the dyes, a small portion of the mixture is put on an absorbent material, such as filter paper. A liquid called a solvent is absorbed onto one end of the filter paper.

The solvent soaks the filter paper, dissolving the ink. If a dye in the ink dissolves well, it will move along the paper at the same rate as the solvent. If another dye in the ink doesn't dissolve as well, it will not move as far.

In a short time, a pattern of colors will appear on the filter paper. Each color will be a single dye that was in the ink. The distance that a component dye travels on the filter paper is a property of that dye. You can use this property to identify dyes that are found in inks of other colors.

Strategy

You will use chromatography to separate the substances in a mixture.
You will show differences in the physical properties of the substances that make up a mixture.

Materials

24-well microplate
filter paper
scissors
pencil
metric ruler
red, green, and black ink marking pens

plastic microtip pipette
ethanol
distilled water
masking tape
resealable plastic bag
paper towel

Procedure

1. Place the 24-well microplate on a flat surface. Arrange the plate so that the numbered columns are at the top and the lettered rows are at the left.
2. Cut three strips of filter paper so that each is approximately as long as the microplate and 1.5 cm wide.

3. Use a pencil to draw a line 1 cm from one end across each strip of filter paper.
4. Make a spot, using the red ink marking pen, in the middle of the pencil line on one of the strips of filter paper. After the ink has dried, apply more ink to the same spot. Allow the ink to dry. See Figure 1.

Figure 1

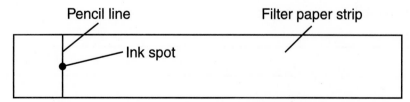

Pencil line   Filter paper strip

Ink spot

Laboratory Activity 1 (continued)

5. Repeat step 4 for the two remaining strips of filter paper. Use the green ink marker to spot one strip and the black ink marker to spot the other.

6. Half-fill the microtip pipette with ethanol. Empty the pipette into well B1 of the microplate.

7. Repeat step 6 using distilled water. Thoroughly mix the ethanol and water in the well.

8. Repeat steps 6 and 7 using wells C1 and D1.

9. Place the end of the first strip of filter paper into well B1 so that the pencil line is about 0.5 cm from the edge of the well. Do not allow the pencil line or spot to come into contact with the solution in the well. The end of the filter paper, however, must be in contact with the solution in the well.

10. Stretch the strip along the top of the microplate. Attach the end of the strip to the microplate with a small piece of tape.

11. Repeat steps 9 and 10 for the two remaining strips using wells C1 and D1.

12. Carefully place the microplate inside the plastic bag and seal the bag. See Figure 2.

13. Observe the spots on the strips of the filter paper. Record your observations in the Data and Observations section.

14. When the solvent reaches the ends of the strips, remove the plate from the plastic bag.

15. Remove the strips from the wells and allow the strips to dry on a paper towel. **WARNING:** *The dyes on the strips can easily stain your hands and clothing; do not touch the colored areas of the strips.*

16. Note the colors of the dyes on each strip. Record these colors in Table 1 for each color of ink used.

17. Attach the dried strips below the Data and Observations section.

Figure 2

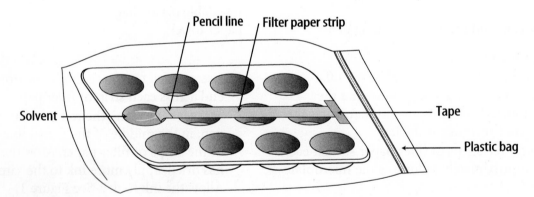

Pencil line   Filter paper strip

Solvent   Tape

               Plastic bag

Data and Observations

Observations of colored spots on strips:

_____

_____

_____

_____

Laboratory Activity 1 (continued)

Table 1

Ink	Color of component dyes
Red	
Green	
Black	

Attach the dried strips of paper here.

Laboratory Activity 1 (continued)

Questions and Conclusions

1. The term *chromatography* is related to the Greek roots *chroma,* meaning color, and *graphos,* meaning written. Use the observations you made during this lab to explain how chromatography reflects the meaning of its roots.

_____

_____

_____

2. Explain if a physical or chemical change took place during the chromatography experiment.

_____

_____

3. What observations would indicate that an ink is made of a single dye?

_____

_____

4. Which component dye traveled the greatest distance for each ink?

Red ink: _____

Green ink: _____

Black ink: _____

5. A student cut out the two colored spots that she observed on the strip of filter paper that had the green ink spot. She placed the two cut-out spots into two wells of the microplate. She then added an equal amount of ethanol and distilled water to each well. She noticed that the solutions in the wells became colored. She repeated the chromatography experiment, spotting each solution on a different strip of filter paper. Predict what she will see on the strips of filter paper after the experiment. Explain your prediction.

_____

_____

_____

_____

Strategy Check

_____ Can you use chromatography to separate the substances in a mixture?

Properties of Matter

Everything that has mass and takes up space is called matter. Matter exists in four different states: solid, liquid, gas, and plasma. This paper, your hand, water, and the air you breathe all consist of matter. Even the planets and stars are made of matter.

Scientists use two types of properties to describe matter. Physical properties depend on the nature of the matter. They are observed when there is no change in chemical composition. The physical properties of water describe it as a colorless, nonmagnetic liquid between the temperatures of 0°C and 100°C. Chemical properties describe the change in chemical composition of matter due to a chemical reaction. A chemical property of water is its reaction with iron to form rust.

Matter is constantly changing. A physical change involves a change in shape, temperature, state, and so on. When a material changes composition, a chemical change occurs.

Strategy

You will classify materials by states of matter.
You will identify physical and chemical properties.
You will distinguish between physical and chemical changes.

Materents

iron sample	magnet	1.5-V dry cells (2)
copper sample	lamp	masking tape
insulated copper wires (3)	test tube	test-tube rack
hydrochloric acid (HCl)	chalk	kitchen matches
toast	dropper	iodine solution
wood sample	rubber sample	

WARNING: *Hydrochloric acid is corrosive, and iodine solution is poisonous. Handle these solutions with care.*

Procedure

Part A—States of Matter

1. Your teacher has set up a bottle containing different materials. Describe the state of matter for each material in the bottle. Record your observations in the Data and Observations section.

Part B—Physical Properties

1. Examine the samples of iron, wood, rubber, and copper. In Table 1, describe the physical properties listed and any other properties you can readily observe.

2. Test each sample for its attraction to a magnet. Record your observations in Table 2.

3. Use 2 fresh dry cells, 3 wires, and a small lamp to test each sample for its ability to conduct electricity. Set up the materials as shown in Figure 1. Use tape to secure each connection. Attach wires to both ends of the sample. Record the conductivity in Table 2. You will know that the sample is a conductor if the bulb lights.

Laboratory Activity 2 (continued)

Part C—Chemical Properties

1. *Safety goggles and a laboratory apron must be worn for this part of the experiment.* Add hydrochloric acid to the test tube until it is about half full. Place a small piece of chalk in the acid and observe what happens. Record your observations in Table 3.
2. Hold a burning match directly over the mouth of the test tube. Record your observations in Table 3.
3. Break a piece of toast to expose the untoasted center. Use a dropper to add a drop of iodine solution to the toasted portion of the toast. Add another drop to the untoasted center. Record your observations in Table 3.

Figure 1

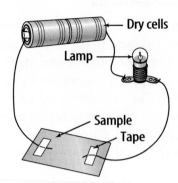

Data and Observations

Part A—States of Matter
States of matter in the bottle:

_____

_____

Part B—Physical Properties

Table 1

Sample	Color	Shape	State of matter	Other properties
iron				
wood				
rubber				
copper				

Laboratory Activity 2 (continued)

Part C—Chemical Properties

Table 2

Sample	Attracted to magnet?	Conducts electricity?
iron		
wood		
rubber		
copper		

Table 3

Materials reacting	Observations
chalk and hydrochloric acid	
iodine and toasted bread	
iodine and untoasted bread	

Questions and Conclusions

1. What states of matter were visible in the bottle? What states were present but invisible in the bottle?

   _____

   _____

   _____

2. What are two physical properties that iron and copper have in common?

   _____

   _____

   _____

3. Why are your observations of the four samples descriptions of physical properties?

   _____

   _____

   _____

4. When you added chalk to hydrochloric acid, what type of change took place? How do you know?

   _____

   _____

Laboratory Activity 2 (continued)

5. List one physical property of the gas created by adding chalk to hydrochloric acid. List one chemical property of this gas.

_____

_____

_____

6. What type of change took place when iodine was dropped on the untoasted bread? How do you know?

_____

_____

_____

Strategy Check

_____ Can you classify materials by states of matter?

_____ Can you identify physical and chemical properties?

_____ Can you distinguish between physical and chemical changes?

Density of a Liquid

All matter has these two properties – mass and volume. Mass is a measure of the amount of matter. Volume is a measure of the space that the matter occupies. Both mass and volume can be measured using metric units. The standard unit of mass in the SI system is the kilogram (kg). To measure smaller masses, the gram (g) is often used. In the metric system, the volume of a liquid is measured in liters (L) or milliliters (mL). Density is a measure of the amount of matter in a given volume of space. Density may be calculated using the following equation.

$$\text{density} = \frac{\text{mass}}{\text{volume}}$$

Density is a physical property of a liquid. By measuring the mass and volume of a sample of a liquid, the liquid's density can be determined. The density of a liquid is expressed as grams per milliliter (g/mL). For example, the density of distilled water is 1.00 g/mL.

Strategy

You will determine the capacity of a pipette.
You will measure the masses of several liquids.
You will calculate the densities of the liquids.
You will compare the densities of the liquids with that of water.

Materials

4 plastic pipettes
metric balance
distilled water
4 small plastic cups
ethanol
corn oil
corn syrup

Procedure

Part A—Determining the Capacity of a Pipette

1. Measure the mass of an empty pipette using the metric balance. Record the mass in the Data and Observations section.
2. Completely fill the bulb of the pipette with distilled water. This can be done as follows:
   a. Pour distilled water into a small plastic cup until it is half full.
   b. Squeeze the bulb of the pipette and insert the stem into the water in the cup.
   c. Draw water into the pipette by releasing pressure on the bulb of the pipette.
   d. Hold the pipette by the bulb with the stem pointed up. Squeeze the bulb slightly to eliminate any air left in the bulb or stem. MAINTAIN PRESSURE ON THE BULB OF THE PIPETTE.

e. Immediately insert the tip of the pipette's stem into the cup of water as shown in Figure.1 Release the pressure on the bulb of the pipette. The pipette will completely fill with water.

Figure 1

Laboratory Activity 1 (continued)

3. Measure the mass of the water-filled pipette. Record this value in the Data and Observations section.

Part B—Determining the Density of a Liquid

1. Completely fill the bulb of another pipette with ethanol as in Step 2 in Part A. Measure the mass of the ethanol-filled pipette. Record this value in Table 1.

Analysis

1. Calculate the mass of water in the water-filled pipette by subtracting the mass of the empty pipette from the mass of the water-filled pipette. Enter this value in the Data and Observations section.
2. The capacity of the pipette, which is the volume of the fluid that fills the pipette, can be calculated using the density of water. Because the density of water is 1.00 g/mL, a mass of 1 g of water has a volume of 1 mL. Thus, the mass of the water in the pipette is numerically equal to the capacity of the pipette. Enter the capacity of the pipette in the Data and Observations section. Record this value in Table 1 as the volume of liquid for each of the liquids used in Part B.
3. Determine the mass of each liquid by subtracting the mass of the empty pipette from the mass of the liquid-filled pipette. Record the values in Table 1.
4. Using the volumes and the masses of the liquids, calculate their densities and record them in the data table.

Data and Observations

Part A—Determining the Capacity of a Pipette

Mass of empty pipette: _____ g

Mass of water-filled pipette: _____ g

Mass of water: _____ g

Capacity of pipette: _____ mL

Part B—Determining the Density of a Liquid

Table 1

Measurement	Liquid		
	Ethanol	**Corn oil**	**Corn syrup**
1. Mass of liquid-filled pipette (g)			
2. Mass of liquid (g)			
3. Volume of liquid (mL)			
4. Density (g/mL)			

Laboratory Activity 1 (continued)

Questions and Conclusions

1. Rank the liquids by their densities starting with the least dense.

   _____

   _____

2. How does the density of water compare to the densities of the other liquids?

   _____

   _____

3. What would you observe if you poured corn oil into a beaker of water? Why?

   _____

   _____

   _____

4. The specific gravity of a substance is the ratio of the density of that substance to the density of a standard, which is water. Specific gravity is a measure of the relative density of a substance. Determine the specific gravity of ethanol, corn oil, and corn syrup.

   _____

   _____

5. Why doesn't specific gravity have units? Determine the specific gravity of ethanol, corn oil, and corn syrup.

   _____

   _____

   _____

Strategy Check

_____ Can you determine the capacity of a pipette?

_____ Can you measure the masses of several liquids?

_____ Can you calculate the densities of the liquids?

_____ Can you compare the densities of the liquids with that of water?

Communicating Your Data

Draw your graph on poster board and present your findings to the class. For more help, refer to the Science Skill Handbook.

The Behavior of Gases

Because most gases are colorless, odorless, and tasteless, we tend to forget that gases are matter. Because the molecules of a gas are far apart and free to move, a gas fills its container. The volume of a gas changes with changes in its temperature and pressure. Gases expand and contract as the pressure on them changes. Gases expand when the pressure on them decreases. They contract when the pressure on them increases. The volume and pressure of a gas are inversely related. Gases also expand and contract as their temperature changes. The expansion of a gas varies directly with its temperature.

Strategy

You will observe how the volume of a gas is affected by a change in pressure.
You will observe how the volume of a gas is affected by a change in temperature.

Materials

methylene blue solution
3 small plastic cups
2 plastic microtip pipettes
water
hot plate, laboratory burner,
   or immersion heater

pliers
5 identical books
metric ruler
24-well microplate

iron or lead washer
masking tape
250-mL beaker

Procedure

Part A—Volume and Pressure of a Gas

1. Place two drops of methylene blue solution in a small plastic cup. Pour water into the cup until it is half full.
2. Fill only the bulb of the plastic pipette with this solution.
3. Seal the tip of the pipette in the following manner: Soften the tip of the pipette by holding the tip near the surface of the hot plate or near the flame of the burner. **WARNING:** *Do not place the tip of the stem on the hot plate or in the flame of the burner. Avoid coming in contact with the hot plate or the flame of the burner.* Away from the heat, squeeze the softened tip of the pipette with the pliers to seal the end. See Figure 1.

4. Place one of the books on the bulb of the pipette and measure in mm the length of the column of air trapped in the stem of the pipette. Record this value in Table 1.
5. Predict what will happen to the length of the trapped air column if another book is placed on top of the first book. Record your prediction in the Data and Observations section.
6. Place another book on top of the first book. Measure, in mm, the length of the column of trapped air and record the measure in Table 1.
7. Continue adding books one at a time, until five books are stacked on top of the pipette. After adding each book, measure the length of the column of trapped air and record the measurement in Table 1.

Figure 1

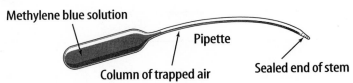

Methylene blue solution

Pipette

Column of trapped air

Sealed end of stem

Laboratory Activity 2 (continued)

Part B—Volume and Temperature of a Gas

1. Fill a well of the microplate with water. Add a few drops of methylene blue solution to the well.

2. Place an iron or lead washer over the end of the stem of the second pipette. Place the bulb in a plastic cup two-thirds filled with water at room temperature. See Figure 2.

Figure 2

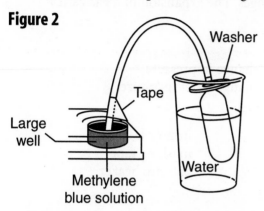

3. Bend the stem of the pipette into the solution in the well of the microplate. With the tip of the stem below the surface of the solution, tape the stem to the side of the microplate. The tip of the stem must remain below the surface of the solution during the remainder of the experiment. See Figure 2.

4. Predict what you will observe if the bulb of the pipette is gently heated. Write your prediction in the Data and Observations section.

5. Heat some water in the 250-mL beaker to a temperature of 30° C.

6. Pour the warmed water into another plastic cup until it is two-thirds full.

7. Remove the bulb of the pipette from the room-temperature water and place it in the warm water in the second cup. Immediately begin counting the bubbles that rise from the tip of the stem submerged in the well of the microplate until it stops bubbling. Record the number of bubbles and the temperature of the water in Table 2.

8. Empty the water from the first plastic cup.

9. Add some water to the beaker and heat the water to a temperature of 35° C. Pour this water into the first plastic cup until it is two-thirds full.

10. Remove the bulb of the pipette from the second cup and place it in the water in the first cup. Count the number of bubbles that rise in the well of the microplate. Record this number and the temperature of the water in Table 2. Empty the water from the second plastic cup.

11. Repeat steps 8–10 for the water that has been heated to 40°C, 45°C, and 50°C .

Analysis

1. Make a graph of your data from Part A using Graph 1. Plot the pressure on the x-axis and the length of the trapped air column on the y-axis. Label the x-axis *Pressure (books)* and the y-axis *Length (mm)*.

2. Complete the third column of Table 2. Make a graph of your data from Part B using Graph 2. Plot the temperature on the x-axis and the total number of bubbles on the y-axis. Label the x-axis *Temperature (°C)* and the y-axis *Total number of bubbles.*

Data and Observations

Part A—Volume and Pressure of a Gas

1. Prediction of length of trapped air column if the pressure on the pipette bulb is increased:

_____

_____

Laboratory Activity 2 (continued)

Table 1

Pressure (number of books)	Length of column of trapped air (mm)
1	
2	
3	
4	
5	

Part B—Volume and Temperature of a Gas

2. Prediction of observations if the air in the bubble is heated:

_____

_____

Graph 1

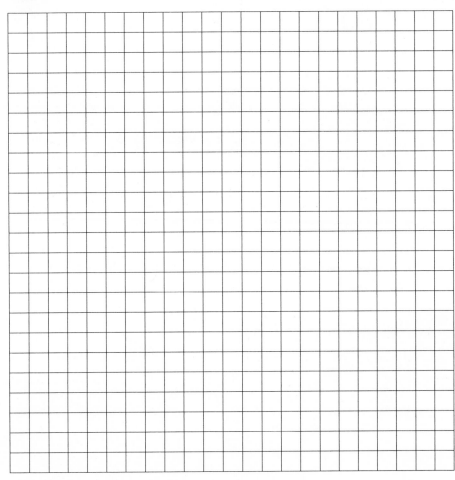

Laboratory Activity 2 (continued)

Table 2

Temperature (°C)	Number of bubbles	Total number of bubbles
_____ (room temp)		
30		
35		
40		
45		
50		

Graph 2

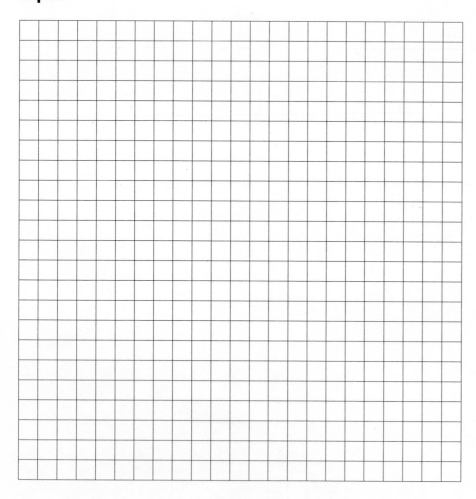

Name _____ Date _____ Class _____

Laboratory Activity 2 (continued)

Questions and Conclusions

1. Explain how the change in the length of the column of trapped air in Part A is a measure of the change in the volume of the air trapped in the pipette.

2. Why did you have to stack identical books on the bulb of the pipette?

3. What is the relationship between the volume and pressure of a gas?

4. Explain why the total number of bubbles produced is a measure of the change in volume of the air that was heated in the bulb of the pipette.

Copyright © Glencoe/McGraw-Hill, a division of the McGraw-Hill Companies, Inc.

Solids, Liquids, and Gases 127

Laboratory Activity 2 (continued)

5. Use your graph to predict the total number of bubbles released if the bulb of the pipette were placed in water at a temperature of 60°C.

_____

_____

6. During each 5°C temperature change, the number of bubbles released was the same. What does this indicate?

_____

_____

_____

7. What is the relationship between the volume and temperature of a gas?

_____

_____

_____

Strategy Check

_____ Can you observe how the volume of a gas is affected by a change in pressure?

_____ Can you observe how the volume of a gas is affected by a change in temperature?

Chemical Activity

The atoms of most chemical elements can either gain or lose electrons during reactions. Elements whose atoms lose electrons during reactions are classified as metals. Metals are found on the left side of the periodic table of elements. The tendency of an element to react chemically is called activity. The activity of a metal is a measure of how easily the metal atom loses electrons.

Strategy

You will observe chemical reactions between metals and solutions containing ions of metals.
You will compare the activities of different metals.
You will rank the metals by their activities.

Materials

96-well microplate
white paper
plastic microtip pipette
distilled water
aluminum nitrate solution, $Al(NO_3)_3 aq$
copper(II) nitrate solution, $Cu(NO_3)_2 aq$
iron(II) nitrate solution, $Fe(NO_3)_3 aq$
magnesium nitrate solution $Mg(NO_3)_2 aq$

nickel nitrate solution, $Ni(NO_3)_2 aq$
zinc nitrate solution, $Zn(A)(NO_3)_2 aq$
8 1-mm × 10-mm strips of each:
    aluminum, Al; copper, Cu; iron, Fe;
    magnesium, Mg; nickel, Ni; and Zinc, Zn
paper towels
hand lens or magnifier

WARNING: *Many of these solutions are poisonous. Avoid inhaling any vapors from the solutions. These solutions can cause stains. Avoid contacting them with your skin or clothing.*

Procedure

1. Place the microplate on a piece of paper on a flat surface. Have the numbered columns of the microplate at the top and the lettered rows at the left.

2. Using the microtip pipette, place 15 drops of the aluminum nitrate solution in each of the wells A1–G1. Rinse the pipette with distilled water.

3. Place 15 drops of copper nitrate solution in each of wells A2–G2 using the pipette. Rinse the pipette with distilled water.

4. Repeat step 1 for each of the remaining solutions. Add the iron nitrate solution to wells A3–G3, the magnesium nitrate solution to wells A4–G4, the nickel nitrate solution to wells A5–G5, the zinc nitrate solution to wells A6–G6. Leave the wells in column 7 empty.

5. Carefully clean each metal strip with a paper towel.

6. Place one strip of aluminum in each of the wells A1–A7.

7. Place one strip of copper in each of the wells B1–B7.

8. Repeat step 5 for the remaining metals. Add the iron strips to wells C1–C7, the magnesium strips to wells D1–D7, the nickel strips to wells E1–E7, and the zinc strips to wells F1–F7. Do not put strips in the wells in row G.

Laboratory Activity 1 (continued)

Figure 1

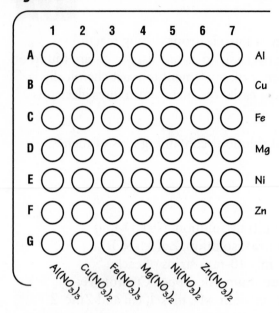

Look for the appearance of deposited materials in the bottom of the well. Each change of appearance of deposits is an indication that a chemical reaction has taken place.

12. If you see an indication of a reaction, draw a positive sign (+) in the corresponding well of the microplate shown in Figure 2 in the Data and Observations section. If you see no indication of a reaction, draw a negative sign (−) in the corresponding well of Figure 2.

9. Figure 1 shows the metal and the solution that are in each of the wells A1–G7.
10. Wait ten minutes.
11. Use a hand lens or magnifier to observe the contents of each well. Look for a change in the color of the solution in each well by comparing it with the color of the solution in well G at the bottom of the column. Look for a change in the texture or color of the metal strip in each well by comparing it with the piece of metal in well 7 near the end of that row.

Figure 2

Well plate grid with rows A–G and columns 1–7.

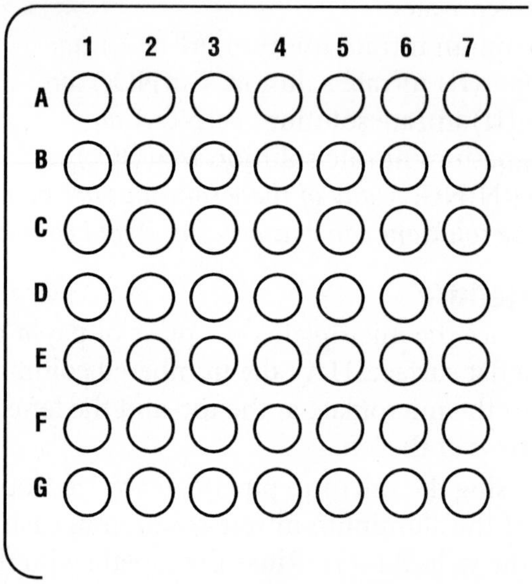

Data and Observations

Count the number of positive signs in each row of wells in Figure 2. Record the value under the corresponding metal in Table 1.

Table 1

Metal	Al	Cu	Fe	Mg	Ni	Zn
Number of reactions						

Laboratory Activity 1 (continued)

Questions and Conclusions

1. Why were solutions but no strips of metal placed in wells G1–G7?

_____

_____

_____

_____

2. Why were strips of metal but no solutions added to wells A7–G7?

_____

_____

_____

_____

3. Why did you clean the metal strips with the paper towel?

_____

_____

_____

_____

_____

4. Using the number of reactions for each metal in Table 1, rank the metals from the most active to the least active.

_____

_____

_____

Strategy Check

_____ Can you determine whether or not a solution is active?

_____ Can you put metals in order based on their activities?

Modeling the Half-Life of an Isotope

Isotopes are atoms of the same element with different atomic masses. These different masses are a result of having different numbers of neutrons in their nuclei. Isotopes can be stable or unstable (radioactive). Radioactive isotopes have unstable nuclei that break down in a process called radioactive decay. During this process, the radioactive isotope is transformed into another, usually more stable, element. The amount of time it takes half the atoms of a radioactive isotope in a particular sample to change into another element is its half-life. A half-life can be a fraction of a second for one isotope or more than a billion years for another isotope, but it is always the same for any particular isotope.

Strategy

You will make a model that illustrates the half-life of an imaginary isotope.
You will graph and interpret data of the isotope's half-life.

Materials

100 pennies
plastic container with lid
timer or clock with second hand
colored pencils

Procedure

1. Place 100 pennies, each head-side up, into the container. Each penny represents an atom of an unstable isotope.
2. Place the lid securely on the container. Holding the container level, shake it vigorously for 20 seconds.
3. Set the container on the table and take off the lid. Remove only the pennies that are now in a tails-up position.
4. Count the pennies you have removed and record this number in Table 1 under *Trial 1.* Also record the number of heads-up pennies that are left.
5. Repeat steps 2 through 4 until there are no pennies left in the container.
6. Repeat steps 1 through 5 and record your data in Table 1 under *Trial 2.*
7. Calculate the averages for each time period and record these numbers in Table 1.

8. Graph the average data from Table 1 on Graph 1. Use one colored pencil to graph the number of heads-up pennies against time. Make a key for the graph that shows this color as *Radioactive Isotopes.* Using a different color of pencil, plot the number of tails-up pennies against time. In your key, show this color as *Stable Atoms.*
9. Record your averages from Table 1 again in Table 2 under *Group 1.*
10. Then, record the averages obtained by other groups in your class in Table 2.
11. Determine the totals for the combined data from all groups in Table 2.
12. Graph this combined data in Graph 2 in the same way as you graphed your group's data in step 8.

Laboratory Activity 2 (continued)

Data and Observations

Table 1

Shaking time	Trial 1		Trial 2		Averages	
	A Number of heads-up remaining	B Number of tails-up removed	C Number of heads-up remaining	D Number of tails-up removed	Columns A and C (H)	Columns B and D (T)
After 20 s						
After 40 s						
After 60 s						
After 80 s						
After 100 s						
After 120 s						
After 140 s						

Table 2

Group Average	Start H*	Start T*	20 s H	20 s T	40 s H	40 s T	60 s H	60 s T	80 s H	80 s T	100 s H	100 s T	120 s H	120 s T	140 s H	140 s T
Group 1	100	0														
Group 2	100	0														
Group 3	100	0														
Group 4	100	0														
Group 5	100	0														
Group 6	100	0														
Group 7	100	0														
Group 8	100	0														
Totals																

Note: H = heads, T = tails

Laboratory Activity 2 (continued)

Graph 1

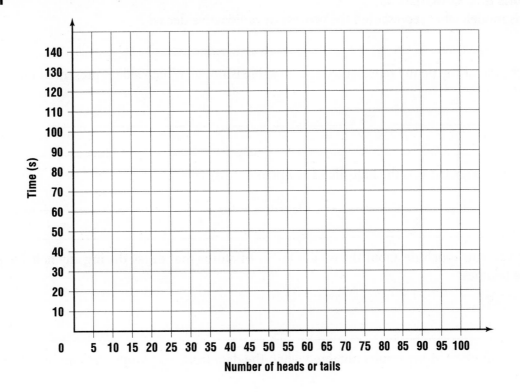

Graph 2

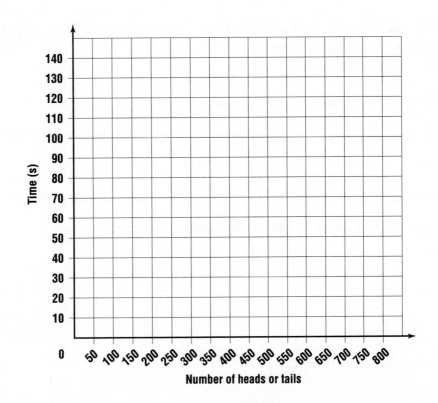

Laboratory Activity 2 (continued)

Questions and Conclusions

1. In this model, what represented the process of radioactive decay?

_____

2. Which side of the penny represented the unstable isotope? Which side represented the stable atom?

_____

_____

3. In this model, what was the half-life of the pennies. Explain.

_____

_____

4. What can you conclude about the total number of atoms that decay during any half-life period of the pennies?

_____

_____

5. Why are more accurate results obtained when the data from all groups was combined and graphed?

_____

_____

6. If your half-life model had decayed perfectly, how many atoms of the radioactive isotope should have been left after 80 seconds?

_____

7. If you started with 256 radioactive pennies, how many would be stable after 60 seconds?

_____

Strategy Check

_____ Can you make a model that illustrates the half-life of an imaginary isotope?

_____ Can you graph and interpret data of the isotope's half-life?

LAB 1 Laboratory Activity

The Effect of Radiation on Seeds

Chapter 18

When seeds are exposed to nuclear radiation, changes may be observed. Seeds contain genetic materials that determine the characteristics of the plants produced from them. Radiation can alter this genetic material. The type of seeds and the amount of radiation absorbed determine the extent of this alteration.

Strategy

You will grow plants from seeds that have been exposed to different amounts of nuclear radiation.
You will observe and record the growth patterns of the plants during a period of a week.
You will use the results of your experiment to discuss some of the possible effects of exposure to nuclear radiation.

Materials

seeds that have received different amounts of radiation
seeds that have not been irradiated

potting soil
boxes or containers for planting

Procedure

1. It is important that all seeds are planted and grown under the same conditions. Plant the seeds according to your teacher's instructions. Plant one container of untreated seeds. Label this container *1*. Carefully label each of the remaining containers. In Table 1, record the number of each container and the amount of radiation the seeds planted in it received.

2. Place the containers in a location away from drafts where they can receive as much light as possible. Keep the soil moist, but not wet, at all times.

3. As soon as the first seeds sprout, start recording your observations in Table 2.

Observe the seeds at regular intervals for a week. If necessary, continue Table 2 on a separate sheet of paper. Watch for variations in sprouting and growth rates and differences in size, color, shape, number, and location of the stems and leaves. Remember, it is important to make an entry in the table for each container at every observation date, even if you report no change.

4. In the space provided in the Data and Observations section, make sketches of your plants and show any variation in growth patterns.

Data and Observations

Table 1

Container number	Amount of radiation
1	no radiation

Laboratory Activity 1 (continued)

Table 2

Date	Container number			

Plant Sketches

Laboratory Activity 1 (continued)

Questions and Conclusions

1. Why did you plant seeds that were not exposed to nuclear radiation?

   _____

   _____

2. What pattern or trends did you observe as the seeds sprouted?

   _____

   _____

   _____

3. What patterns or trends did you observe in the growth rate of the plants?

   _____

   _____

   _____

   _____

4. What relationship can be seen between the amount or time of radiation exposure and the following:

   maximum height of plants

   _____

   size of leaves

   _____

   color of leaves

   _____

   shape of leaves

   _____

   number of leaves

   _____

   placement of leaves

   _____

   other variations that you observed

   _____

   _____

   _____

Laboratory Activity 1 (continued)

5. What characteristics of the plants seem unaffected?

_____

_____

_____

_____

6. What conclusions can you make based on the results of this experiment?

_____

_____

_____

_____

_____

7. What predictions can you make based on the results of this experiment?

_____

_____

_____

_____

Strategy Check

_____ Can you grow plants from seeds that have been exposed to different amounts of nuclear radiation?

_____ Can you observe and record the growth patterns of the plants during a period of weeks?

_____ Can you use the results of your experiment to discuss some possible effects of exposure to nuclear radiation?

Radioactive Decay— A Simulation

Certain elements are made up of atoms whose nuclei are naturally unstable. The atoms of these elements are said to be radioactive. The nucleus of a radioactive atom will decay into the nucleus of another element by emitting particles of radiation. It is impossible to predict when the nucleus of an individual radioactive atom will decay. However, if a large number of nuclei are present in a sample, it is possible to predict the time period in which half the nuclei in the sample will decay. This time period is called the half-life of the element.

Radioactive materials are harmful to living tissues. Their half-lives are difficult to measure without taking safety precautions. To eliminate these problems, you will simulate the decay of unstable nuclei by using harmless materials that are easy to observe. In this experiment you will use dried split peas to represent the unstable nuclei of one element. Dried lima beans will represent the stable nuclei of another element. Your observations will allow you to make a mental model of how the nuclei of radioactive atoms decay.

Strategy

You will simulate the decay of a radioactive element.
You will graph the results of the simulated decay.
You will determine the half-life of the element.

Materials

small bag of dried split peas
250-mL beaker
large pizza or baking tray
bag of dried lima beans

Procedure

1. Count out 200 dried split peas and place them in a beaker.
2. Record the number of split peas in Table 1 as Observation 0.
3. Place the pizza or baking tray on a flat surface.
4. Hold the beaker over the tray and sprinkle the split peas onto the tray. Try to produce a single layer of split peas on the tray.
5. Remove all the split peas that have NOT landed on the flat side down. Count the split peas that you have removed and return them to the bag. Replace the number of peas that you have removed from the tray with an equal number of lima beans. Count the number of peas and the number of lima beans on the tray. Record these values in Table 1 as Observation 1.

6. Scoop the peas and beans from the tray and place them into the beaker.
7. Predict how many split peas you will remove if you repeat steps 4 and 5. Enter your predictions in the Data and Observations section.
8. Repeat steps 4 through 6, recording your data in the data table as Observation 2.
9. Predict how many observations you will have to make until there are no split peas remaining. Enter your prediction in the Data and Observations section.
10. Repeat steps 4 through 6 until there are no split peas remaining.

Laboratory Activity 2 (continued)

Data and Observations

Table 1

Observation	Time (minutes)	Split peas	Lima beans

Prediction of number of split peas removed:

_____

Prediction of number of observations until there are no split peas remaining:

_____

Laboratory Activity 2 (continued)

Analysis

In this experiment each split pea represents the nucleus of an atom of radioactive element A. A split pea that has landed flat side down represents the nucleus of an atom of radioactive element A that has not yet decayed. Each split pea that has NOT landed flat side down represents the nucleus of element A that has decayed. Each lima bean represents the nucleus of an element B that was formed by the decay of the nucleus of an element A .

Assume that the time period between each observation was 5 minutes. Observation 1 will have been made at 5 minutes, observation 2 at 10 minutes, and so on. Complete the time column in Table 1.

1. Use Graph 1 below to graph the results of your experiment. Plot on one axis the number of the nuclei of element A atoms remaining after each observation. Plot the time of this observation on the other axis. Determine which variable should be represented by each axis.

2. Use Graph 1 to construct another graph. Plot on one axis the number of nuclei of element B atoms remaining after each observation. Plot the time of the observation on the other axis.

3. Determine the appropriate half-life of element A from your graph.

Graph 1

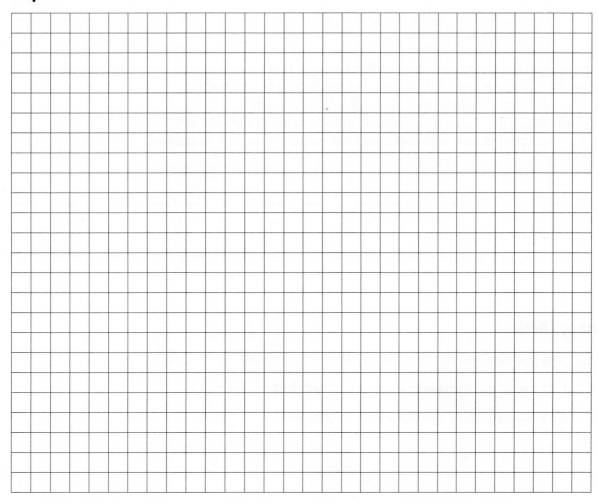

Laboratory Activity 2 (continued)

Questions and Conclusions

1. What is the approximate half-life of element A?

2. Use your graph to determine the number of element A nuclei remaining after 2 half-lives, and after 3 half-lives.

3. Why did you replace split peas but not lima beans during this experiment?

4. The two graphs that you constructed look like mirror-images. Explain why this is so.

5. Suppose you were given 400 dried split peas to do this experiment. Explain which of the following questions you could answer before starting this experiment.
   a. Can you identify which split peas will fall flat side up?
   b. Can you predict when an individual split pea will fall flat side up?
   c. Can you predict how many split peas will remain after 3 observations?

Strategy Check

_____ Can you simulate the decay of a radioactive element?

_____ Can you graph the results of the simulated decay?

_____ Can you determine the half-life of the element?

LAB 1 — Laboratory Activity

Preparation of Carbon Dioxide

Chapter 19

When you burn a material that contains carbon, such as paper or gasoline, carbon dioxide gas is produced. You also produce carbon dioxide when your body "burns" the food you eat. You don't burn the food with a flame, however. The cells of your body combine the carbon in the food you eat with the oxygen in a reaction called oxidation. When carbon compounds are oxidized, carbon dioxide gas is produced.

Carbon dioxide gas is colorless, odorless, and tasteless. It is necessary for photosynthesis, the process by which green plants produce oxygen and glucose.

Strategy

You will observe a reaction that produces carbon dioxide gas.
You will describe the reaction that produces carbon dioxide gas.
You will observe the chemical properties of carbon dioxide gas.

Materials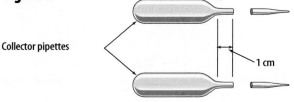

metric ruler	hydrochloric acid solution	forceps
distilled water	24-well microplate	marble chips
lime water	scissors	transparent tape
toothpicks	long stem plastic pipette	plastic microtip pipettes (4)
matches		

WARNING: *Hydrochloric acid is corrosive. Avoid its contact with your skin or clothing. Rinse spills with water.*

Procedure

Part A—Preparing Carbon Dioxide Gas

1. Place the microplate on a flat surface. Have the numbered columns of the microplate at the top and the lettered rows at the left.
2. Use the scissors to trim the stem of the long stem pipette to a length of 2.5 cm.
3. Using the scissors, cut a small slit in the pipette as shown in Figure 1.

Figure 1

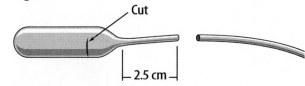

Cut

2.5 cm

4. Use the forceps to insert a small marble chip through the slit into the bulb of the pipette. Cover the slit with transparent tape to seal the bulb. Place the bulb of the pipette in well A1.
5. Make collector pipettes by cutting the stems of 2 of the microtip pipettes to lengths of 1 cm, as shown in Figure 2.

Figure 2

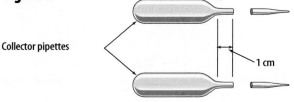

Collector pipettes

1 cm

6. Completely fill the two collector pipettes with water by holding each pipette under running water with its stem upward. Squeeze the bulb repeatedly until there is no more air in the pipette.
7. Stand the collector pipettes with their stems upward in wells C1 and C2.
8. Using an uncut microtip pipette, add about half a pipettefull of hydrochloric acid to well C3. Rinse the pipette with distilled water.
9. Take the pipette containing the marble chip from well A1 and invert it.

Laboratory Activity 1 (continued)

10. Squeeze out the air. Place the stem of the pipette in well C3 and draw the hydrochloric acid into the bulb of the pipette. Immediately invert the pipette.

11. Take the collector pipette from well C1 and invert it over the stem of the pipette containing the hydrochloric acid and marble chip. Insert the stem of the lower pipette into the stem of the collector pipette. Place the stem of the lower pipette into the bulb of the collector pipette as far as it will go. Place the pipettes into well C4 as shown in Figure 3. Allow the displaced water from the upper pipette to collect in the well.

12. Observe the reaction of the marble chip and hydrochloric acid. Record your observations in the Data and Observations section.

13. Allow the bulb and about 0.5 cm of the stem of the collector pipette to fill with gas. Remove the collector pipette and invert it. Allow the water to form a "plug" sealing the gas in the pipette as shown in Figure 4.

14. Return the collector pipette to well C1.

15. Remove the second collector pipette from well C2 and the pipette containing the hydrochloric acid and the marble chip from well C4.

16. Repeat steps 11 and 13. Return the second collector pipette to well C2.

Figure 3

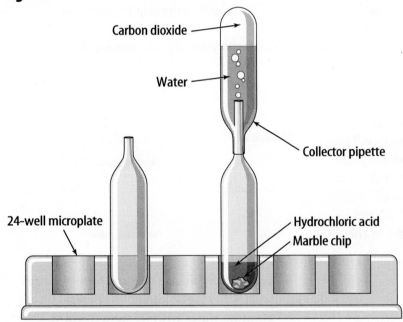

Carbon dioxide

Water

Collector pipette

24-well microplate

Hydrochloric acid

Marble chip

Figure 4

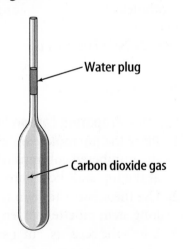

Water plug

Carbon dioxide gas

Laboratory Activity 1 (continued)

Part B—Properties of Carbon Dioxide Gas

1. Fill a clean microtip pipette with the lime water.
2. Observe the color of the lime water. Record your observations in the Data and Observations section.
3. Push the tip of the microtip pipette into the stem of the collector pipette in well C1. Push the tip through the water plug and into the bulb of the collector pipette.
4. Add about one-fourth a pipettefull of the lime water to the collector pipette. Remove the upper pipette.
5. Remove the collector pipette from well C1. Cover the tip of the pipette with your finger and shake the pipette vigorously for about 20 seconds.

6. Return the pipette to well C1. Observe the color of the solution. Record your observations in the Data and Observations section.
7. Ignite the tip of a toothpick with a match. **CAUTION:** *Use care with open flames.* Extinguish the flame, allowing the tip of the toothpick to glow.
8. Remove the water plug from the collector pipette in well C2 by gently squeezing the bulb of the pipette.
9. Immediately insert the glowing tip of the toothpick into the bulb of the collector pipette.
10. Observe the tip of the toothpick. Record your observations in the Data and Observations section.

Data and Observations

Part A—Preparing Carbon Dioxide Gas

Step 12. Observations of reaction of marble chip and hydrochloric acid

_____

_____

Part B—Properties of Carbon Dioxide Gas

Step 2. Observations of lime water

_____

_____

Step 6. Observations of solution

_____

_____

Step 10. Observations of glowing tip of toothpick in carbon dioxide gas

_____

_____

Laboratory Activity 1 (continued)

Questions and Conclusions

1. When carbon dioxide gas and lime water are mixed, calcium carbonate is formed. Describe how your observations of the reaction of lime water and carbon dioxide gas can be used to identify carbon dioxide gas.

   _____

   _____

2. Carbon dioxide gas does not support combustion. Describe how your observations of the glowing toothpick can be used to identify carbon dioxide gas.

   _____

   _____

   _____

3. When a can of a soft drink is opened, bubbles of carbon dioxide gas form. When hydrochloric acid and marble chips are mixed, bubbles of carbon dioxide gas are produced. How do the two situations differ?

   _____

   _____

   _____

   _____

Strategy Check

_____ Can you describe the reaction that produces carbon dioxide gas?

LAB 2 Laboratory Activity

Preparation of Oxygen

Chapter 19

About 20 percent of Earth's atmosphere is oxygen. Oxygen gas is colorless, odorless, and tasteless. You, as well as most living organisms, require oxygen for respiration.

On Earth, most metallic elements are found as oxides. An oxide is a compound containing oxygen and another element. One oxide with which you are familiar is silicon dioxide—sand. Sand and water are the most common compounds of oxygen on this planet's surface.

Strategy

You will observe a reaction that produces oxygen gas.
You will describe the reaction that produces oxygen gas.
You will observe the chemical properties of oxygen gas.

Materials

24-well microplate	cobalt nitrate solution	toothpicks
plastic microtip pipettes (3)	metric ruler	matches
household bleach solution	scissors	
distilled water	long-stem plastic pipette	

WARNING: *Bleach and cobalt nitrate solution can cause stains; avoid contact with your skin or clothing. Rinse spills with water.*

Procedure

Part A—Preparing Oxygen Gas

1. Place the microplate on a flat surface. Have the numbered columns of the microplate at the top and the lettered rows at the left.
2. Using a clean microtip pipette, add 30 drops of the household bleach to well A1. Rinse the pipette with distilled water.
3. Using the microtip pipette, add 10 drops of the cobalt nitrate solution to well A2. Rinse the pipette with distilled water.

4. Make collector pipettes by cutting the stems of two of the microtip pipettes to lengths of 1 cm, as shown in Figure 1.
5. Completely fill the two collector pipettes with water by holding each pipette under running water with its stem upward. Squeeze the bulb repeatedly until there is no more air in the pipette.
6. Stand the collector pipettes with their stems upward in wells C1 and C2.

Figure 1

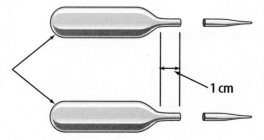

Collector pipettes

1 cm

Figure 2

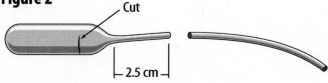

Cut

2.5 cm

Laboratory Activity 2 (continued)

7. Use the scissors to trim the stem of the long stem pipette to a length of 2.5 cm as shown in Figure 2.

8. Using this pipette, draw up all the bleach solution from well A1 into the bulb of the pipette.

9. Hold the pipette with the stem upward. Gently squeeze out the air. While still squeezing the bulb, invert the pipette and place the stem into well A2. Draw the cobalt nitrate solution into the bulb of the pipette. Immediately invert the pipette.

10. Take the collector pipette from well C1 and invert it over the stem of the pipette containing the bleach and cobalt nitrate solutions. Insert the stem of the lower pipette into the stem of the collector pipette. Place the stem of the lower pipette into the bulb of the collector pipette as far as it will go. Place the pipettes into well C4 as shown in Figure 3. Allow the displaced water from the upper pipette to collect in the well.

11. Observe the reaction of the bleach and cobalt nitrate solutions. Record your observations in the Data and Observations section.

12. Allow the bulb and about 0.5 cm of the stem of the collector pipette to fill with gas. Remove the collector pipette and invert it. Allow the water to form a "plug" sealing the gas in the pipette as shown in Figure 4.

13. Return the collector pipette to well C1.

14. Remove the second collector pipette from well C2 and the pipette containing the bleach and cobalt nitrate solutions from well C4.

15. Repeat steps 10 and 12. Return the collector pipette to well C2.

Figure 3

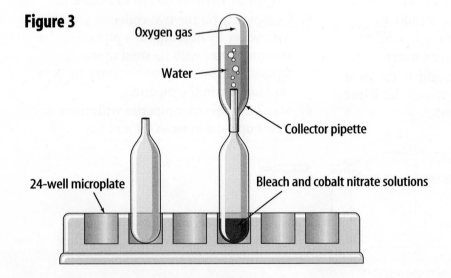

Oxygen gas

Water

Collector pipette

24-well microplate

Bleach and cobalt nitrate solutions

Figure 4

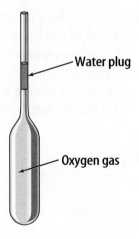

Water plug

Oxygen gas

Laboratory Activity 2 (continued)

Part B—Properties of Oxygen Gas

1. Ignite the tip of a toothpick with a match. **CAUTION:** *Use care with open flames.* Extinguish the flame.
2. Remove the water plug from the collector pipette in well C1 by gently squeezing the bulb of the pipette.
3. Immediately insert the glowing tip of the toothpick into the bulb of the collector pipette.

4. Observe the reaction. Record your observations in the Data and Observations section.
5. Repeat steps 1 through 4 for the second collector pipette in well C2.

Data and Observations

Part A—Preparing Oxygen Gas

Step 11. Observations of reaction of bleach and cobalt nitrate solutions:

_____

_____

Part B—Properties of Oxygen Gas

Step 4. Observations of glowing toothpick in presence of oxygen gas:

_____

_____

Questions and Conclusions

1. Describe how your observations of the reaction of the glowing toothpick and oxygen gas demonstrate a property of oxygen gas.

_____

_____

_____

2. What is the chemical formula of oxygen gas?

_____

3. The wood of the toothpick contains carbon compounds. What substances are formed when these carbon compounds burn?

_____

Laboratory Activity 2 (continued)

4. You observed the chemical reaction of sodium hypochlorite which is found in bleach, and cobalt nitrate solutions. The chemical formula for sodium hypochlorite is NaOCl. The chemical formula for cobalt nitrate is $Co(NO_3)_2$.

   a. What elements are in each compound?

   _____

   _____

   b. How many oxygen atoms are in each compound?

   _____

Strategy Check

_____ Can you describe the reaction that produces oxygen gas?

The Five Solutions Problem

Chapter 20

Do you recall the seven dwarfs in the story of Snow White? Their names reflected their behaviors. One could recognize them by their actions. Substances can also be identified by their behaviors. One way of identifying a substance is by observing how it reacts with other known substances. In any chemical reaction, new substances are produced. State, color, and other physical properties of substances produced in a chemical reaction can help identify the substances that reacted.

In this experiment, you will classify solutions by how the substances in the solutions react. Using this classification, you will identify an unlabeled sample of one of these solutions.

Strategy

You will observe the reactions of five different known solutions, two at a time.
You will classify your observations.
You will identify an unlabeled sample of one of these solutions.

Materials

96-well microplate
white paper
7 plastic microtip pipettes
dilute hydrochloric acid, $HCl(aq)$
iron(III) nitrate solution, $Fe(NO_3)_3(aq)$
silver nitrate solution, $AgNO_3(aq)$

sodium carbonate solution, $Na_2CO_3(aq)$
sodium iodide solution, $NaI(aq)$
plastic cup
distilled water
sample of unknown solution 1, 2, 3, 4, or 5

WARNING: *Many of these solutions are poisonous. Avoid inhaling any vapors from the solutions. Silver nitrate solution and sodium iodide solution can cause stains. Avoid any contact between them and your skin or clothing.*

Procedure

Part A—Observing Reactions of Known Solutions

1. Wear aprons, gloves, and goggles during this experiment.
2. Place the microplate on a piece of white paper on a flat surface. Have the numbered columns of the microplate at the top and the lettered rows at the left.
3. Using a microtip pipette, place four drops of the hydrochloric acid solution in each of wells A1 through F1.
4. Using a clean pipette, place four drops of the iron(III) nitrate solution in each of wells A2 through F2.
5. Repeat step 4 for each of the remaining four solutions. Use a clean pipette for each.

Place the silver nitrate solution in wells A3 through F3, the sodium carbonate solution in wells A4 through F4, and the sodium iodide solution in wells A5 through F5.

6. Fill the plastic cup with distilled water, and thoroughly rinse each pipette. Discard the water.
7. Add four drops of the hydrochloric acid solution to each of wells A1 through A5.
8. Using another clean pipette, add four drops of iron(III) nitrate to each of wells B1 through B5.

Laboratory Activity 1 (continued)

9. Repeat step 8 for the remaining solutions. Use a clean pipette for each solution. Add the silver nitrate solution to wells C1 through C5, the sodium carbonate solution to wells D1 through D5, and the sodium iodide solution to wells E1 through E5. Figure 1 shows the solutions in each of the wells A1 through E5.

10. Observe the contents of each well. Note any changes in the physical properties of the substances in each well. Record your observations in Table 1.

Part B—Identifying an Unknown Solution

1. Obtain a small sample of an unknown solution from your teacher. Record the number of the solution sample in the first column of Table 2.

2. Use a clean microtip pipette to add four drops of the sample solution to each of the wells F1 through F5.

3. Observe the contents of each well. Note any changes in the physical properties of the contents in each well. Record your observations in Table 2.

4. Compare the changes that occurred in wells containing the unknown solution with the changes that occurred in wells containing the known solutions.

Figure 1

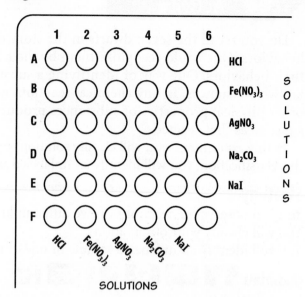

SOLUTIONS

Data and Observations

Part A—Observing Reactions of Known Solutions

Table 1

Solution in microplate	Solution added				
	HCl	Fe(NO₃)₃	AgNO₃	Na₂CO₃	NaI
1. HCl					
2. Fe(NO₃)₃					
3. AgNO₃					
4. Na₂CO₃					
5. NaI					

Laboratory Activity 1 (continued)

Part B—Identifying an Unknown Solution

Table 2

Unknown solution	Solution				
	HCl	Fe(NO$_3$)$_3$	AgNO$_3$	Na$_2$CO$_3$	NaI

Questions and Conclusions

1. What is the identity of the sample solution?

_____

_____

_____

_____

_____

2. What properties of the substances that were formed helped you to identify your sample solution?

_____

_____

_____

_____

_____

3. How did the reactions between the solutions in wells A1 through E5 help you to identify the sample solution?

_____

_____

_____

_____

_____

Laboratory Activity 1 (continued)

4. Could you use the results of your observations in Part A to identify a solution that is not one of the five solutions? Explain.

_____

_____

_____

_____

_____

Strategy Check

_____ Can you classify your observations?

_____ Can you identify an unlabeled sample by the way it reacts with known substances?

Laboratory Activity

Investigating Covalent and Ionic Bonds

Chapter 20

All substances are made of atoms. Some of the physical and chemical properties of a substance are determined by the chemical bonds that hold its atoms together. In this experiment you will investigate the properties of compounds formed by two types of chemical bonds—covalent bonds and ionic bonds.

The atoms of covalent compounds are held together by covalent bonds. A covalent bond forms when two atoms share electrons. In other substances, atoms transfer electrons and form ions. An ion is an atom that has gained or lost electrons. In ionic compounds, the ions are held together by ionic bonds.

Solutions of ionic compounds can conduct an electric current. These solutions of covalent compounds conduct an electric current. A measure of how well a solution can carry an electric current is called conductivity.

Strategy

You will determine the conductivity of several solutions.

You will classify the compounds that were dissolved in the solutions as ionic compounds or covalent compounds.

Materials

9-V battery and battery clip
10-cm × 10-cm cardboard sheet
masking tape
4 alligator clips
1000-Ω resistor
LED (light-emitting diode)
2 20-cm lengths of insulated copper wire
24-well microplate

7 plastic pipettes
sulfuric acid solution, $H_2SO_4(aq)$
sodium chloride solution, $NaCl(aq)$
sodium hydroxide solution, $NaOH(aq)$
silver nitrate solution, $AgNO_3(aq)$
glucose solution, $C_6H_{12}O_6(aq)$
glycerol solution, $C_3H_8O_3(aq)$
distilled water

WARNING: *Sulfuric acid and sodium hydroxide can cause burns. Silver nitrate can cause stains. Avoid inhaling any vapors from the solutions. Avoid any contact between the solutions and your skin or clothing.*

Procedure

Part A—Constructing a Conductivity Tester

1. Attach the 9-V battery clip to the 9-V battery. Use tape to attach the battery securely to the cardboard sheet, as shown in Figure 1.

2. Attach an alligator clip to one of the lead wires of the 1000-Ω resistor. Connect the same alligator clip to the red lead wire of the battery clip. Tape the resistor and alligator clip to the cardboard sheet as shown in Figure 2.

Figure 1

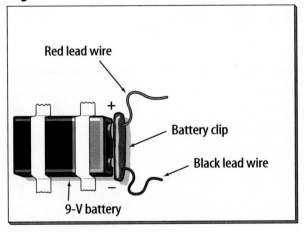

Red lead wire

Battery clip

Black lead wire

9-V battery

Copyright © Glencoe/McGraw-Hill, a division of the McGraw-Hill Companies, Inc.

Laboratory Activity 2 (continued)

3. Attach an alligator clip to the *long* lead wire of the light-emitting diode (LED). Connect this alligator clip to the second wire of the 1000-Ω resistor. Tape the alligator clip to the cardboard sheet.

4. Attach an alligator clip to the *short* lead wire of the LED. Connect this alligator clip to one end of the insulated copper wires. Tape the alligator clip to the cardboard sheet as shown in Figure 3.

5. Attach the last alligator clip to one end of the second insulated copper wire. Connect the alligator clip to the *black* lead wire of the battery clip. Tape the alligator clip to the cardboard sheet as shown in Figure 4.

6. Check to be certain that the alligator clips, resistor, and battery are securely taped to the cardboard sheet and that the clips are not touching one another.

7. Have your teacher check your conductivity tester.

8. Touch the two ends of the two insulated copper wires, and observe that the LED glows.

Figure 3

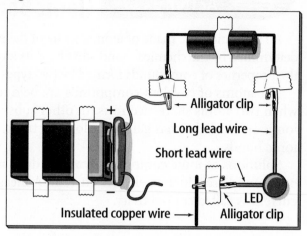

Figure 2

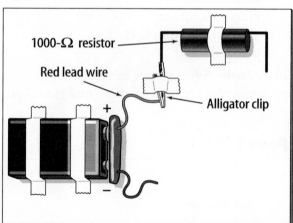

Figure 4

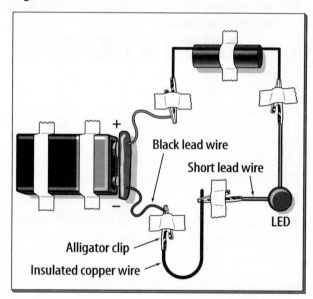

Laboratory Activity 2 (continued)

Part B—Testing the Conductivity of a Solution

1. Wear an apron, gloves, and goggles for Part B of the experiment.
2. Place the microplate on a flat surface. Have the numbered columns of the microplate at the top and the lettered rows at the left.
3. Using a clean pipette, add a pipettefull of the sulfuric acid solution to well A1.
4. Using another clean pipette, add a pipettefull of the sodium chloride solution to well A2.
5. Repeat step 4 for each remaining solution. Use a clean pipette for each solution. Add the sodium hydroxide solution to well A3, the silver nitrate solution to well A4, the glucose solution to well A5, and the glycerol solution to well A6.
6. Using a clean pipette, add a pipettefull of distilled water to well A7. Figure 5 shows the contents of each of the wells A1 through A7.

7. Place the exposed ends of the two insulated copper wires into the solution in well A1, positioning the wires so they are at opposite sides of the well. Be sure that the exposed ends of the wires are completely submerged.
8. Observe the LED. Use the brightness of the LED as an indication of the conductivity of the solution. Rate the conductivity of the solution using the following symbols: + (good conductivity); − (fair conductivity); or 0 (no conductivity). Record your rating in the corresponding well of the microplate shown in Figure 6.
9. Remove the wires and dry the ends of the wires with a paper towel.
10. Repeat steps 6 through 9 for each remaining solution and the distilled water.

Figure 5

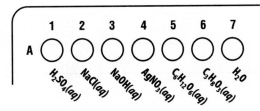

Data and Observations

Figure 6

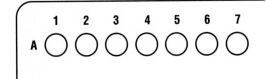

Laboratory Activity 2 (continued)

Questions and Conclusions

1. What is the conductivity of distilled water?

_____

2. Why was the conductivity of the distilled water measured?

_____

_____

_____

3. What characteristic is common to the compounds that produce solutions that can conduct electricity?

_____

_____

4. What characteristic is shared by the compounds that produce solutions that do not conduct an electric current?

_____

_____

5. How do the conductivities of solutions of ionic compounds and covalent compounds compare?

_____

_____

_____

Strategy Check

_____ Can you determine the conductivity of solutions?

_____ Can you classify compounds in solutions as ionic or covalent?

Conservation of Mass

Chapter 21

In a chemical reaction, the total mass of the substances formed by the reaction is equal to the total mass of the substances that reacted. This principle is called the law of conservation of mass, which states that matter is not created or destroyed during a chemical reaction.

In this experiment, sodium hydrogen carbonate, $NaHCO_3$ (baking soda), will react with hydrochloric acid, HCl. The substances formed by this reaction are sodium chloride, NaCl; water, H_2O; and carbon dioxide gas, CO_2.

Strategy

You will show that new substances are formed in a chemical reaction.
You will show the conservation of mass during a chemical reaction.

Materials

sealable plastic sandwich bag containing sodium hydrogen carbonate, $NaHCO_3$
hydrochloric acid, HCl
plastic pipette
paper towel
metric balance

Procedure

1. Obtain the plastic sandwich bag containing a small amount of sodium hydrogen carbonate.
2. Fill the pipette with the hydrochloric acid solution. Use a paper towel to wipe away any acid that might be on the outside of the pipette. Discard the paper towel. **WARNING:** *Hydrochloric acid is corrosive. Handle with care.*

3. Carefully place the pipette in the bag. Press the bag gently to eliminate as much air as possible. Be careful not to press the bulb of the pipette. Seal the bag. See Figure 1.
4. Measure the mass of the sealed plastic bag using the metric balance. Record this value in the Data and Observations section.
5. Remove the plastic bag from the balance. Without opening the bag, direct the stem of the pipette into the sodium hydrogen carbonate. Press the bulb of the pipette and allow the hydrochloric acid to react with the sodium hydrogen carbonate. Make sure that all the acid mixes with the sodium hydrogen carbonate.
6. Observe the contents of the bag for several minutes. Record your observations in the Data and Observations section.
7. After several minutes, measure the mass of the sealed plastic bag and its contents. Record this value in the Data and Observations section.

Figure 1

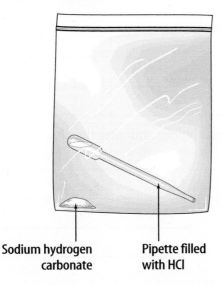

Sodium hydrogen   Pipette filled
carbonate   with HCl

Laboratory Activity 1 (continued)

Data and Observations

Table 1

Mass of plastic bag before reaction (in grams)	
Observations from Step 6	
Mass of plastic bag after reaction (in grams)	

Questions and Conclusions

1. Why was it important for the plastic bag to be sealed?

_____

_____

_____

_____

_____

_____

2. What did you observe that indicated that a chemical reaction took place?

_____

_____

_____

_____

_____

3. Compare the mass of the plastic bag and its contents before and after the chemical reaction.

_____

_____

_____

_____

_____

Laboratory Activity 1 (continued)

4. Does your comparison in Question 3 confirm the conservation of mass during this chemical reaction? Explain.

_____

_____

_____

_____

_____

Strategy Check

_____ Can you demonstrate that new substances are formed in a chemical reaction?

_____ Can you show the conservation of mass during a chemical reaction?

Chemical Reactions

Chapter 21

The changes that occur during a chemical reaction are represented by a chemical equation. In an equation, chemical symbols represent the substances involved. The reactants are the substances that react. The products are the substances formed from the reaction. For example, reaction of the elements sodium and chlorine to produce sodium chloride is shown by the following chemical equation.

$$2Na(s) + Cl_2(g) \rightarrow 2NaCl(s)$$

reactants   *product*

In a synthesis reaction, two or more substances react to form a new substance. You may think of a synthesis reaction as putting substances together to produce a new substance. The synthesis reaction that produces hydrogen peroxide is given by the equation below.

$$2H_2O(l) + O_2(g) \rightarrow 2H_2O_2(l)$$ *Synthesis reaction*

A decomposition reaction produces several products from the breakdown of a single compound. This process is similar to breaking a single compound into several simpler compounds and/or elements.

$$2H_2O(l) \rightarrow 2H_2(g) + O_2(g)$$ *Decomposition reaction*

In a single-displacement reaction, one element replaces another element in a compound. In the following reaction carbon displaces the hydrogen in water, forming gaseous carbon monoxide, and hydrogen is released as hydrogen gas.

$$H_2O(l) + C(s) \rightarrow H_2(g) + CO(g)$$ *Single-displacement reaction*

Strategy

You will recognize the reactants and products of a chemical reaction.
You will identify the type of chemical reaction you observe.
You will write a word equation for a chemical reaction.
You will write a balanced chemical equation using chemical symbols.

Materials

Part A	Part B	Part C
aluminum foil	aluminum foil	string
burner	burner	iron nail, Fe
matches	matches	beaker
steel wool, Fe	test tube	copper (II), sulfate solution, $CuSO_4$
tongs	spoon	watch or clock
	baking soda, $NaHCO_3$	paper towel
	test tube holder	

WARNING: *Copper(II) sulfate solution is poisonous. Handle with care. Wear goggles and apron.*

Laboratory Activity 2 (continued)

Procedure

Part A—Synthesis Reaction

1. Protect the table with a sheet of aluminum foil. Place the burner in the center of the foil. Light the burner. **WARNING:** *Stay clear of the flame.*

2. Observe the color of the steel wool. Record your observations in the Data and Observations section.

3. Predict if there will be any changes in the steel wool if it is heated in the flame. Write your prediction in the Data and Observations section.

4. Hold the steel wool (containing iron, Fe) with the tongs over the flame as shown in Figure 1. As the steel wool burns, record any changes you observe.

5. Take the steel wool out of the flame and let it cool. Record your observations.

Figure 1

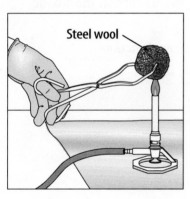

Steel wool

Part B—Decomposition Reaction

1. Set up a burner as in step 1 of Part A.

2. Place a spoonful of baking soda, $NaHCO_3$, in a test tube. In the Data and Observations section, write your prediction of what will happen as the baking soda is heated. Use the test-tube holder to heat the test tube in the flame, as shown in Figure 2. Do not point the mouth of the test tube at anyone.

Figure 2

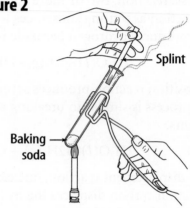

Splint

Baking soda

3. Record the description and colors of the products formed inside the tube.

4. Test for the presence of CO_2. Light a wooden splint. Hold the flaming splint in the mouth of the test tube. If the flame of the splint goes out, CO_2 is present. Record your observations of the products of this reaction.

Laboratory Activity 2 (continued)

Part C—Single Displacement Reaction

Figure 3

1. Tie a string around the nail. Fill a beaker about half full with the CuSO₄ solution. Record the colors of the nail and the CuSO₄ solution in Table 1. **WARNING:** *The CuSO₄ solution is toxic. Handle with care.*

2. Predict what changes will happen to the appearance of the nail and the solution when mixed. Record your prediction in the Data and Observations section. Dip the nail in the CuSO₄ as shown in Figure 3. After 5 minutes, pull the nail from the solution and place it on a paper towel. Record the colors of the nail and the solution in Table 1.

3. Put the nail back into the solution and observe further color changes.

Data and Observations

Part A—Synthesis Reaction

1. Prediction of changes in heated steel wool:

2. Color of steel wool before burning:

3. Color of burned steel wool:

Part B—Decomposition Reaction

1. Prediction of changes in heated baking soda:

2. Description of deposits inside heated test tube:

3. Observations of flaming splint:

Part C—Single Displacement Reaction

1. Prediction of changes in nail and CuSO₄ solution:

Laboratory Activity 2 (continued)

Table 1

Observation time	Color of nail	Color of CuSO₄ solution
Before reaction		
After reaction		

Questions and Conclusions

1. Write a word equation to describe the reaction of the heated steel wool and oxygen.

   _____ plus _____, in the presence of heat,

   yields _____.

2. Write a balanced equation using chemical symbols for the synthesis reaction of iron and oxygen.

   _____

3. Write a word equation to describe the decomposition reaction of baking soda.

   _____ yields _____ plus _____ plus water.

4. Write a chemical equation using symbols for the decomposition of sodium bicarbonate, or

   baking soda. _____

5. Write a word equation to describe the single-displacement reaction of iron and copper sulfate.

   _____

6. Write a chemical equation using symbols for the single-displacement reaction of iron and

   copper(II) sulfate. _____

Strategy Check

_____ Can you recognize the reactants and products of a chemical reaction?

_____ Can you identify the type of chemical reaction you observe?

_____ Can you write a word equation for a chemical reaction?

_____ Can you write a balanced chemical equation using chemical symbols?

Examining Properties of Solutions

To make a saltwater solution, you can use either table salt or rock salt. If the mass of each sample is the same, the salt with the greater surface area—table salt—will dissolve faster. Other factors affect the speed of the dissolving process. For example, temperature and stirring will slow down or speed up the dissolving of solute. In addition, the speed at which gases dissolve is affected by changes in pressure.

Strategy

You will explain the effects of particle size, temperature, and stirring on a solid in solution.
You will explain the effects of temperature, stirring, heating, and pressure on a gas in solution.

Materials

clear plastic cups (6)
graduated cylinder (100-mL)
table salt (3 g)
rock salt (3 g)
paper towels
stirring rod

watch with second hand or seconds mode
bottle of soda water, unopened
beaker (500-mL)
hot tap water
cold water

WARNING: *Do not taste, eat, or drink any materials used in the lab.*

Procedure

Part A—Solid in Solution

1. Label the six plastic cups A through F. Use the graduated cylinder to add 100 mL of hot tap water each to cups A and B. Add 100 mL of cold water each to cups C, D, E, and F.
2. Divide each type of salt into three equal samples.
3. Add a salt sample to each cup (one at a time) as indicated in Figure 1.

When adding each sample, observe closely and record the time required for the salt to dissolve completely. See Figure 1. When no salt particles are visible, record the time for that sample in Table 1.

4. Rate the salt samples from fastest to slowest in dissolving. Give the fastest dissolving sample a rating of 1, the slowest, a 6. Record your ratings in Table 1.

Figure 1

	A	B	C	D	E	F
Type of salt	table	rock	table	rock	table	rock
Water temperature	hot	hot	cold	cold	cold	cold
Stirred?	no	no	no	no	yes	yes

Laboratory Activity 1 (continued)

Part B—Gas in Solution

1. Rinse cups A, B, and C with water.
2. Observe the unopened bottle of soda water. Open the bottle and observe it again. Compare your observations, and record your comparison in Part B of the Data and Observations section.
3. Pour hot water from the tap into the 500-mL beaker until it is about half full.

4. Add 25 mL of soda water to each of the three cups. Stir the soda water in cup B. See Figure 2. Place cup C in the beaker of hot water. Leave cup A as your control. Compare the speed of bubbling in each cup. Record your observations in Table 2.

Figure 2

  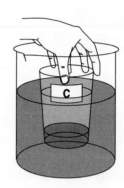

Data and Observations

Part A—Solid in Solution

Table 1

Cup	Salt sample	Water conditions	Time (s)	Rating
A	table salt	hot		
B	rock salt	hot		
C	table salt	cold		
D	rock salt	cold		
E	table salt	cold, stirred		
F	rock salt	cold, stirred		

Laboratory Activity 1 (continued)

Part B—Gas in Solution
Observations of unopened and opened bottle:

_____

_____

_____

Table 2

Cup	Soda conditions	Observations and comparison of bubbling
A	control	
B	stirred	
C	heated	

Questions and Conclusions

1. How does particle size affect the rate at which salt dissolves in water?

_____

_____

_____

_____

2. How does temperature affect the speed of the dissolving process of salt in water?

_____

_____

_____

_____

3. How does stirring affect the speed of the dissolving process of salt in water?

_____

_____

_____

_____

Laboratory Activity 1 (continued)

4. How did you create a pressure change in the bottle of soda water? What happened as a result of this pressure change?

_____

_____

_____

_____

5. What factors cause the speed of bubbling in soda water to increase?

_____

_____

_____

_____

6. Most soft drinks contain dissolved CO_2. Sometimes when you shake a bottle of soft drink and then open it, the soft drink shoots into the air. Explain why this happens.

_____

_____

_____

_____

_____

_____

Strategy Check

_____ Can you explain the effects of particle size, temperature, and stirring on a solid in solution?

_____ Can you explain the effect of temperature, stirring, and pressure on a gas in solution?

How soluble are two salts at varying temperatures?

LAB 2 Laboratory Activity

Perhaps the most familiar type of solution is a solid dissolved in water. When you add lemonade mix to water, you make lemonade, a water solution. No chemical change takes place when a solid is dissolved in a liquid. If the liquid evaporates, the original solid remains and it is chemically unchanged.

The maximum amount of a solute that can be dissolved in a solvent is called the solubility of the solute. Solubility of a solid is often expressed as the maximum number of grams of a substance that will dissolve in 100 g of solvent. The solubility of a substance is not the same under all conditions. For example, temperature changes can affect the solubility of a solid in water.

Strategy

You will determine the solubility of two salts.
You will determine the effect of temperature on the solubility of a salt.
You will interpret information from a solubility graph.

Materials

graduated cylinder (10-mL)
beaker (250-mL)
hot plate
thermometer
4 test tubes
test-tube rack
test-tube holder

pot holder
4 small aluminum pie pans
metric balance
sodium chloride, NaCl(*cr*) (2 5-g samples per group)
potassium bromide, KBr
tap water
distilled water

WARNING: *KBr is a body tissue irritant. Handle the thermometer carefully. Do not stir with the thermometer. If it breaks, do not touch anything. Inform your teacher immediately.*

Procedure

1. Safety goggles and a laboratory apron should be worn throughout this experiment. Pour tap water into the beaker until it is about one-third full. Heat the water on the hot plate until the temperature reaches 55°C–60°C. Use the thermometer to determine the temperature.

2. Label the four test tubes A, B, C, and D. Label the four aluminum pans A, B, C, and D. Find the mass of each pan and record it Table 1.

3. Get the four 5-g salt samples from your teacher. Add 5 g of NaCl to each of tubes A and B. Add 5 g of KBr to each of tubes C and D.

4. Using the graduated cylinder, add 5 mL of distilled water to each of tubes A through D.

Shake each tube to dissolve the salt, but be careful to avoid spilling the solution.

5. Carefully place tubes A and C in the water in the beaker and allow the contents to reach the temperature of the water bath, which will take about 5 min. Use the test-tube holder to remove the hot tubes to the test-tube rack. **WARNING:** *The tubes will be hot.*

6. Allow the four tubes to stand in the test-tube rack for a few minutes to allow any solid material to settle.

7. Using the test-tube holder, carefully pour the liquid from tube A into pan A. Do not transfer any of the solid. You will need to pour the liquid slowly. See Figure 1. Pour the liquids from the remaining tubes into the pans in the same way.

Laboratory Activity 2 (continued)

Figure 1

8. Determine the mass of each pan and its liquid. Record the masses in the table in the Data and Observations section.

9. Heat the pans on a hot plate using low heat. When all of the liquid evaporates, use a pot holder to remove the pans from the heat. **CAUTION:** *Do not touch the hot pans or the hot plate.* After the pans have cooled, find the mass of each and record this information in the table.

10. Determine the mass of the liquid evaporated from each pan by subtracting the mass of the pan and salt after evaporation from the mass of the pan, liquid, and salt. Record this information in the table.

11. Determine the mass of salt left in each pan after evaporation by subtracting the mass of the empty pan from the mass of the pan and salt. Record this information in the table.

12. Use the masses of the dissolved salts to determine the solubility per 100 g of water. Use a proportion in your calculations. Record the solubility in the table.

Data and Observations

Object being massed	Mass (g)			
	A	**B**	**C**	**D**
Empty pan				
Pan liquid, and salt				
Pan and salt				
Liquid evaporated				
Salt after evaporation				
Solubility				

Laboratory Activity 2 (continued)

Questions and Conclusions

1. What type of solid material settled to the bottom of each test tube?

    _____

    _____

2. Which salt had the greater solubility at 55°C–60°C?

    _____

3. What would you expect to happen to the solubility of each salt if the temperature of the water were increased to 75°C?

    _____

4. Look at the solubility graph in Figure 2. This graph shows how change in temperature affects the solubility of four common compounds.

Figure 2

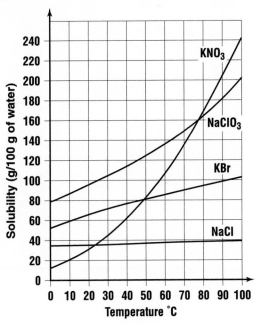

a. How does an increase in the temperature affect the solubility of NaCl?

    _____

    _____

b. How does an increase in temperature affect the solubility of KBr?

    _____

    _____

Laboratory Activity 2 (continued)

5. Refer to Figure 2. At what temperature does KNO_3 have the same solubility as KBr? What is the solubility at this temperature?

_____

_____

Strategy Check

_____ Can you determine the solubility of NaCl and KBr?

_____ Can you determine how temperature affected the solubility of NaCl and KBr?

_____ Can you interpret information from a solubility graph?

Acids, Bases, and Indicators

You can express the acidity of a solution by using a pH scale. The pH of a solution is a measure of the concentration of the hydronium ions (H_3O^+) in that solution. The pH scale ranges in value from 0 to 14. Acids have pH values less than 7. Bases have pH values greater than 7. A neutral solution has a pH value of exactly 7.

The pH of a solution can be determined by using an indicator. An indicator is usually an organic compound that changes color at certain pH values. A universal indicator is a mixture of indicators that can be used to determine a wide range of pH values.

Strategy

You will investigate how a universal indicator is affected by acidic and basic solutions. You will determine the pH of several common liquids.

Materials

96-well microplate
sheet of white paper
plastic microtip pipette
distilled water

0.1M hydrochloric acid solution, HCl(*aq*)
0.01M sodium hydroxide solution, NaOH(*aq*)

universal indicator solution
samples of lemon juice, milk, and liquid soap

WARNING: *The sodium hydroxide and hydrochloric acid are corrosive. The universal indicator can cause stains. Avoid contacting these solutions with your skin or clothing. Wear an apron and goggles during this experiment.*

Procedure

Part A—Preparing a Color Scale

1. Place the 96-well microplate on a piece of white paper on a flat surface. Have the numbered columns of the microplate at the top and the lettered rows at the left.

2. Using the microtip pipette, add 9 drops of the distilled water to each of the wells A2–A11.

3. Use the pipette to add 10 drops of the hydrochloric acid solution to well A1. Rinse the pipette with distilled water.

4. Use the pipette to add 10 drops of the sodium hydroxide solution to well A12. Rinse the pipette with distilled water.

5. Use the pipette to transfer one drop of hydrochloric acid solution from well A1 to well A2. Return any solution remaining in the pipette to well A1, making sure the pipette is empty. Mix the contents of well A2 by drawing the solution into the pipette and then returning it to well A2.

6. Using the pipette, transfer one drop of the solution in well A2 to well A3. Return any solution remaining in the pipette to well A2.

Mix the contents of well A3 by drawing the solution into the pipette and then returning it to the well.

7. Repeat step 6, transferring A3 into A4, A4 into A5, and A5 into A6. Rinse the pipette with distilled water.

8. Use the pipette to transfer one drop of sodium hydroxide solution from well A12 to A11. Return any sodium hydroxide solution remaining in the pipette to well A12. Mix the contents of well A11 by drawing the solution into the pipette and then returning it to well A11.

9. Using the pipette, transfer one drop of the solution in well A11 to A10. Return any solution remaining in the pipette to well A11. Mix the contents of well A10 by drawing the solution into the pipette and then returning it to the well.

Laboratory Activity 1 (continued)

10. Repeat step 9 for wells A10 and A9. Do not transfer solution from well A8 to well A7. Well A7 will contain only distilled water. Rinse the pipette with distilled water.

11. Use the pipette to add 1 drop of the universal indicator to each of the wells A1–A12. Rinse the pipette with distilled water.

12. Observe the solutions in each well. Record the color of the solution in each well in Table 1 in the Data and Observations section.

Part B—Determining the pH of Solutions

1. Use the pipette to place 9 drops of lemon juice in well C1. Rinse the pipette with distilled water.

2. Place 9 drops of milk in well C2 and 9 drops of liquid soap in well C3. Rinse the pipette in distilled water after each addition.

3. Using the pipette, add 1 drop of the universal indicator to each of the wells C1–C3.

4. Observe the solution in each well. Record the name of the solution and its color in Table 2.

Part C—Analysis

1. By adding 1 drop of the hydrochloric acid solution in well A1 to the 9 drops of water in well A2, the concentration of the hydrochloric acid in well A2 was reduced to 1/10 that of well A1. With each dilution in wells A1–A6, you reduced the concentration of the acid from one well to the next by 1/10. Likewise, by diluting the sodium hydroxide solution, the concentration of the sodium hydroxide solution is decreased by 1/10 from wells A12–A8. Because of these dilutions, the pH value of the solution in each of the wells A1–A12 will be the same as the number of the well, as shown in Figure 1. For example, the pH of the solution in well A3 will be 3.

2. The color of the solutions in wells A1–A12 can be used to determine the pH of other solutions that are tested with the universal indicator. You can determine the pH of a solution by comparing its color with the color of the solution in wells A1–A12. Using Table 1, determine the pH values of the solutions that you tested in Part B of the procedure. Record the pH values in Table 2.

Figure 1

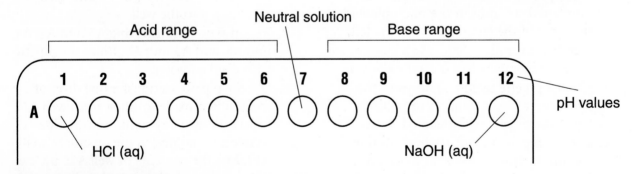

Data and Observations

Table 1

Well	A1	A2	A3	A4	A5	A6
Color						
Well	A7	A8	A9	A10	A11	A12
Color						

Laboratory Activity 1 (continued)

Table 2

Solution	Color	pH

Questions and Conclusions

1. What is the range of pH values of acids and bases?

   _____

2. Classify the solutions that you tested in Part B as acids or bases.

   _____

3. Distilled water is neutral. What is its pH value? What color will water appear if it is tested with the universal indicator solution?

   _____

   _____

4. What is a universal indicator?

   _____

   _____

Strategy Check

_____ Can you determine how acidic and basic solutions affect a universal indicator?

_____ Can you determine the pH of several common liquids?

Acid Rain

LAB 2 Laboratory Activity

Have you ever seen stained buildings, crumbling statues, or trees that have lost their leaves because of acid rain? Acid rain is a harmful form of pollution. Its effects are also easy to see. Acid rain is precipitation that contains high concentrations of acids. The precipitation may be in the form of rain, snow, sleet, or fog.

The major products formed from burning fossil fuels such as coal and gasoline are carbon dioxide and water. However, nitrogen dioxide and sulfur dioxide are also formed. These gases dissolve in precipitation to form acid rain.

When acid rain falls on a pond or lake, the acidity of the water increases. The rise in the acidity is usually harmful to organisms living in the water. If the acidity becomes too high, all living things in the water will die. The pond or lake is then considered to be "dead."

Strategy

You will generate a gas that represents acid rain.
You will observe the reaction of this gas with water.
You will demonstrate how the gas can spread from one location to another.

Equipment

96-well microplate
plastic microtip pipette
distilled water
paper towel
universal indicator solution

forceps
calcium carbonate, $CaCO_3(cr)$
scissors
soda straw
sealable, plastic sandwich bag

white paper
hydrochloric acid solution, $HCl(aq)$
watch or clock

WARNING: *The hydrochloric acid solution is corrosive. The universal indicator solution can cause stains. Avoid contacting these solutions with your skin or clothing. Wear an apron and goggles during this experiment.*

Procedure

1. Place the microplate on a flat surface.
2. Using the plastic microtip pipette, completely fill all the wells except A1, A12, D6, H1, and H12 with distilled water.
3. Use a paper towel to wipe away any water on the surface of the microplate.
4. Using the microtip pipette, add 1 drop of the indicator solution to each well containing water. Rinse the microtip pipette with distilled water.
5. Use the forceps to add a small lump of calcium carbonate to well D6.
6. Use the scissors to cut four 1-cm lengths of soda straw. Insert one length of soda straw in each of the wells A1, A12, H1, and H12 as shown in Figure 1. Cut a 0.5-cm length of soda straw and place it in well D6.
7. Carefully place the microplate into the plastic sandwich bag and seal the bag. Place the bag on the piece of white paper.

8. Using the scissors, punch a small hole in the plastic bag directly over well D6.
9. Fill the microtip pipette one-fourth full with the hydrochloric acid solution.
10. Slip the tip of the pipette through the hole above well D6. Direct the stem of the pipette into the soda straw in well D6.
11. Add 4 drops of hydrochloric acid to the well. Observe the surrounding wells.
12. After 30 seconds, note any color changes in the surrounding wells. Record a color change in the solution in a well by marking a positive sign (+) in the corresponding well of the microplate shown in Figure 2a in Data and Observations.
13. Repeat steps 11 and 12 two more times. Record your two sets of observations in Figure 2b and Figure 2c, respectively.

Laboratory Activity 2 (continued)

Figure 1

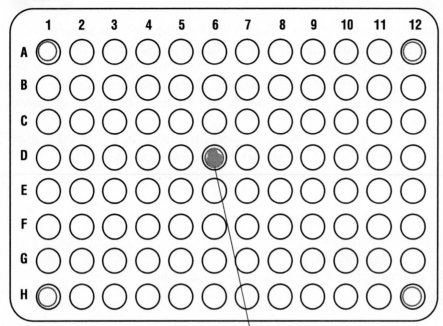

Calcium carbonate

Data and Observations

Figure 2a

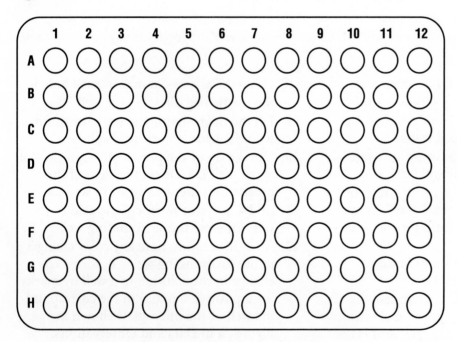

Laboratory Activity 2 (continued)

Figure 2b

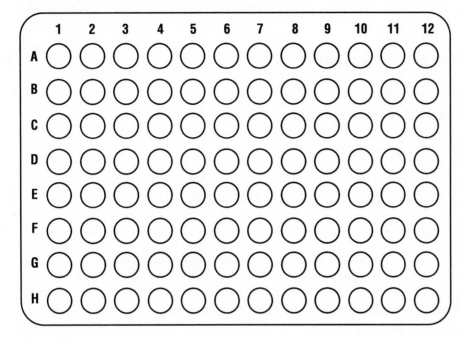

Figure 2c

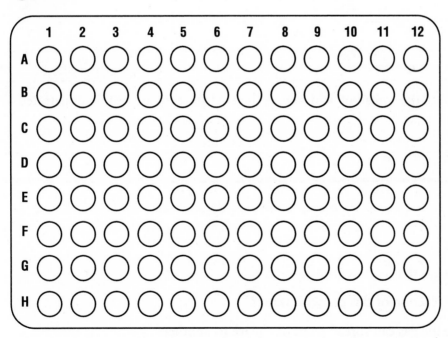

Laboratory Activity 2 (continued)

Questions and Conclusions

1. Calcium carbonate and hydrochloric acid react to produce a gas. What is the gas?

_____

2. What does this gas represent in this experiment?

_____

3. What physical process caused the gas to move through the air in the plastic bag?

_____

_____

4. Why were the lengths of soda straws placed in wells A1, A12, H1, and H12?

_____

_____

_____

5. Discuss how this experiment demonstrates how acid rain can spread from the source of the chemicals that produce acid rain to other areas.

_____

_____

_____

_____

6. What factors that may cause the spread of acid rain in the environment are not demonstrated in this model experiment?

_____

_____

_____

Strategy Check

_____ Can you generate a gas that represents acid rain?

_____ Can you detect the reaction of this gas with water?

_____ Can you show how the gas can spread from one place to another?

The Breakdown of Starch

LAB 1 Laboratory Activity

Chapter 24

Living things are made of carbon compounds called organic compounds. Many organic compounds are long molecules called polymers, which consist of small repeating units. Starch is a polymer of sugar units.

When you eat a piece of bread, your body breaks down the starch present in the bread. Substances in your saliva begin splitting the long starch polymers into shorter chains of sugar units. Digestion continues in your stomach and intestines until the shorter chains are broken down into individual sugar molecules. Finally, the sugar molecules combine with oxygen inside the cells to produce carbon dioxide and water and release energy. This energy allows you to run, stay warm, talk, think, and so on.

Strategy

You will use indicators to test unknown solutions for starch and sugar.
You will use a solution of saliva substitute to detect the breakdown of starch.

Materials

4 test tubes
solution X
solution Y
test-tube holder
starch indicator solution

sugar indicator solution
test-tube rack
250-mL beaker
thermometer
100-mL beaker

saliva substitute
4 rubber stoppers for test tubes
watch or clock

WARNING: *Starch indicator solution and sugar indicator solution are poisonous. Handle with care.*

Procedure

Part A—Starch and Sugar Indicators

1. Label the four test tubes A through D. Look at Table 1. Add 10 drops of unknown solution as indicated in Table 1 to the corresponding test tube. See Figure 1.

Figure 1

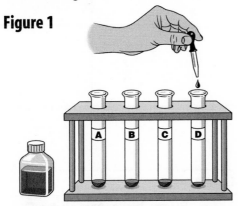

2. Use the test-tube holder to place tubes B and D in the boiling water bath provided by your teacher.
3. Add 1 drop of starch indicator solution to tubes A and C. If the indicator changes color, starch is present.

4. Record the color change in Table 1 and indicate which solution contains starch.
5. Add 1 drop of sugar indicator solution to tubes B and D and boil for 3 minutes. **WARNING:** *Tubes will be hot.* If the indicator changes color, sugar is present. Record the color changes in Table 1, and indicate which solution contains sugar. Using the test-tube holder, remove tubes B and D from the boiling water bath and place them in the rack to cool.
6. Rinse the test tubes with water.

Part B—Breakdown of Starch

1. Prepare a warm water bath in a 250-mL beaker. Make a mixture of warm and cool water to fill the beaker about half full. Use the thermometer to determine the temperature of the water. Add small amounts of warm or cool water using the 100-mL beaker until the temperature of the water bath reaches 35°C–40°C.

Laboratory Activity 1 (continued)

2. Use the test tube labeled A from Part A. Fill the test tube about 1/4 full with a solution of saliva substitute.

3. You tested solutions X and Y to determine which contained starch. Add 15 drops of the starch solution to the saliva substitute solution in the test tube. Stopper and shake the tube to mix the liquids. Note the time. Remove the stopper and place the tube in the warm water bath. See Figure 2.

4. After 5 minutes, pour two small and equal portions of the liquid in tube A into tubes B and C. Do not use all the liquid from tube A.

5. Using the procedure in Part A, not including step 1, place tube C in the boiling water bath. Test the liquid in tube B for the presence of starch with one drop of starch indicator solution. Test the liquid in Tube C with a drop of sugar indicator solution. Record your observations of color changes in Table 2. Continue to time the reaction in tube A.

Figure 2

6. Leave tube A in the warm water bath. Add warm or cool water to the bath to adjust the bath temperature to 35°C–40°C.

7. Rinse tubes B and C with water.

8. After another 5 minutes, repeat steps 4–6. If time allows, repeat these steps a total of three times. Record your observations each time in Table 2.

Data and Observations

Part A—Starch and Sugar Indicators

Table 1

Tube	Unknown solution	Indicator solution	Color change	Starch (X)	Sugar (X)
A	X	starch			
B	X	sugar			
C	Y	starch			
D	Y	sugar			

Part B—Breakdown of Starch

Table 2

Time (min)	Color Changes	
	Starch indicator—tube B	Sugar indicator—tube C
5		
10		
15		

Laboratory Activity 1 (continued)

Questions and Conclusions

1. What happened to the starch solution when added to the saliva substitute? How do you know this?

   _____

   _____

   _____

   _____

2. Why is a water bath at a temperature between 35°C and 40°C used in this experiment?

   _____

   _____

   _____

3. If you chew a plain cracker without adding sugar, you will probably detect a sweet taste. Why does this happen?

   _____

   _____

   _____

   _____

4. Can the indicator solutions used in this experiment be used to determine how much sugar or starch is present in a sample? If so, explain how this could be done. If not, explain why this cannot be done.

   _____

   _____

   _____

Strategy Check

_____ Can you test unknown solutions for starch and sugar?

_____ Can you detect the breakdown of starch?

Testing for a Vitamin

LAB 2 Laboratory Activity

Vitamin C is a complex organic compound found in many foods, such as fruits and vegetables. You can identify vitamin C by its chemical properties. It reacts with certain indicator solutions, causing the solutions to change color. The color change of the solution indicates that the vitamin C in the solution has reacted. You can determine the relative amounts of vitamin C in different foods by testing the food with the indicator solutions.

Strategy

You will observe the reactions of various concentrations of vitamin C with a color indicator. You will compare the relative amounts of vitamin C in different types of orange juice and orange drink.

Materials

96-well microplate   vitamin C indicator
sheet of white paper   freshly squeezed orange juice
plastic microtip pipette   bottled orange juice
vitamin C solution   orange drink
distilled water

WARNING: *The vitamin C indicator can cause stains. Avoid contacting it with your skin or clothing.*

Procedure

Part A—Testing the Vitamin C Solution

1. Place the 96-well microplate on a piece of white paper on a flat surface. Have the numbered columns of the microplate at the top and the lettered rows at the left.
2. Using the microtip pipette , add 10 drops of the vitamin C solution to well A1. Rinse the pipette with distilled water.
3. Use the pipette to add 5 drops of distilled water to each of the wells A2–A6.
4. Remove most of the solution from well A1 using the pipette. Add 5 drops of this solution to well A2. Return the solution remaining in the pipette to well A1. Rinse the pipette with distilled water.
5. Use the pipette to mix and then remove most of the contents of well A2. Add 5 drops of this solution to well A3. Return the solution remaining in the pipette to well A2. Rinse the pipette with distilled water.
6. Repeat step 5 for wells A4–A6 as shown in Figure 1.

Figure 1

7. Using the pipette, add 3 drops of vitamin C indicator solution to each of the wells A1–A6. Stir the contents of each well with a clean toothpick.
8. Observe the color of each well. If you see a color change, mark a positive sign (+) in the corresponding well of the microplate shown in Figure 2 in the Data and Observations section. Record no change in color as a zero (0).
9. Rinse the pipette with distilled water.

Laboratory Activity 2 (continued)

Part B—Testing Orange Juices for Vitamin C

1. Add 10 drops of freshly squeezed orange juice to well B1 using the pipette. Rinse the pipette with distilled water.
2. Add 5 drops of distilled water to each of the wells B2–B6.
3. Mix and then remove most of the contents of well B2 using the pipette. Add 5 drops of this solution to well B3. Return the solution remaining in the pipette to well B2. Rinse the pipette with distilled water.
4. Repeat step 3 for wells B3–B6.

5. Add 3 drops of the vitamin C indicator solution to each of the wells B1–B6. Stir the contents of each well with a clean toothpick.
6. Observe the color of each well. Record your observations of wells B1–B6 by marking a + or 0 in the corresponding wells shown in Figure 2.
7. Rinse the pipette with distilled water.
8. Repeat steps 1–7 for the bottled orange juice and the orange drink. Place the orange juice in well C1 and the orange drink in well D1.

Data and Observations

Figure 2

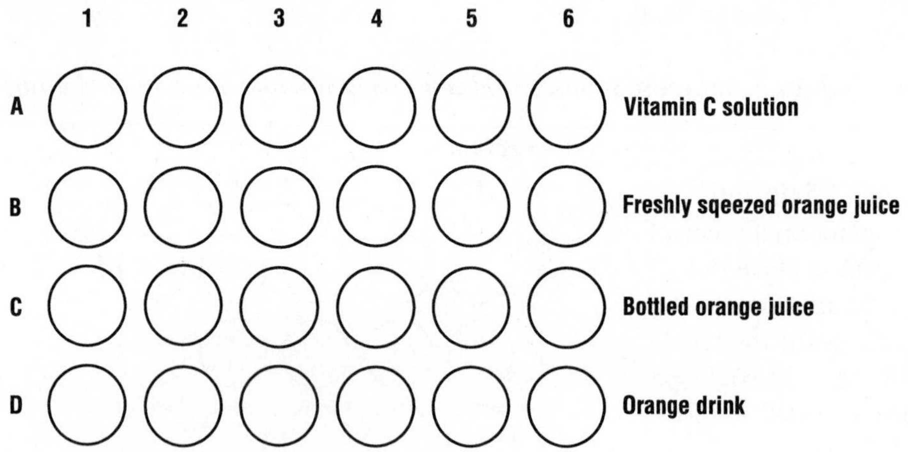

Vitamin C solution

Freshly sqeezed orange juice

Bottled orange juice

Orange drink

Analysis

A color change indicates that vitamin C is present in the solution.

Questions and Conclusions

1. What happens to the concentration of the solutions in the wells as one moves across a row?

_____

2. Which solution had the greatest concentration of vitamin C? How do you know?

_____

_____

_____

Laboratory Activity 2 (continued)

3. Which of the three food products tested had the greatest concentration of vitamin C?

_____

_____

4. A sample of freshly squeezed orange juice contains 5.0 mg of vitamin C in 15 mL of the juice. How much juice must you drink to meet a daily recommended requirement of 32 mg of vitamin C?

_____

5. Vitamin C reacts with oxygen in the air. How does the length of time orange juice is exposed to air affect the amount of vitamin C in it? Design an experiment to answer this question.

_____

_____

_____

Strategy Check

_____ Can you determine the concentration of vitamin C in a substance?

_____ Can you determine the amounts of vitamin C in different types of orange juice and orange drink?

Soldering with an Alloy

LAB 1 Laboratory Activity

Solder (SOD er) is a very useful household alloy. It is used to patch or join metals in items ranging from jewelry and crafts to metal pipes to electrical circuits and broken wires. It is inexpensive and easy to find in hardware stores. Its relatively low melting point and quick solidifying make it easy to use. A soldering tool provides the heat to melt the solder. This tool is usually a special rod of metal that is attached to an electrical wire. The tip of the soldering tool becomes heated according to the proper temperature for the type of solder that is used. Hard solders contain combinations of silver, copper, and zinc. Soft solders are the most common and contain between 30 to 70 percent tin with other compounds, usually lead. In this lab you will examine a tin solder and make an electrical connection with it.

Strategy

You will observe and describe the properties of tin solder.
You will use solder to connect copper wires.

Materials

copper wire cut into two 15-cm lengths
tin solder wire (about 15 cm long)
soldering tool

ceramic tile (large one for placing soldering tool and wires on)
aluminum foil

Procedure

1. Place students into groups of three or four. Examine the properties of the solder wire. Look for ductility, malleability, color, and luster. Refer to the information given in the Data and Observations section. Choose a number to represent the property and record your observations in the table provided.

2. Repeat the same procedure for the copper wire.

3. Take a tile and completely cover it in aluminum foil. Ceramic tile is used as a non-conducting type of material. Completely cover the tile with aluminum to prevent any soldering from eventually sticking to it.

4. Plug in your soldering tool and set it to heat up to tin soldering. If you have the type of soldering tool with no temperature settings, just let it heat up for about five minutes. **WARNING:** *Do not touch the metal end of the tool.* The colored plastic end is made so that it will conduct heat and is safe to hold.

5. Place your soldering tool on the covered tile and wait for it to heat. **WARNING:** *Point the hot tip away from any papers or flammable materials. It will burn a hole through clothing so remove all jackets and backpacks from the lab table.*

6. Collect two pieces of copper wire and place them end to end on your tile. Have one member of the group hold the wires in place. Have another hold the length of solder at the exact place where the two copper wires meet. The point is to make the solder a liquid metal for just a second so that it will bond the two pieces of copper wire together.

7. A third student should just barely touch the tip of the tool to the place where the solder meets the copper wire. It may take some practice getting the solder to melt and stick to the copper wire. Professional electricians practice for years before they make small and efficient solder connections.

8. When you have successfully soldered the two pieces of copper wire together, show the finished product to your teacher. You now have a wire that will conduct electricity and is twice as long as when you started. You have effectively used an alloy for repair purposes.

Laboratory Activity 1 (continued)

Data and Observations

Malleability:
1 – 2 = not malleable
3 – 4 = slightly malleable
5 – 6 = malleable
7 – 8 = very malleable
9 – 10 = highly malleable (unable to keep a shape for very long)
Ductility:
1 – 2 = not ductile
3 – 4 = slightly ductile
5 – 6 = ductile
7 – 8 = very ductile
9 – 10 = highly ductile
Luster:
1 – 2 = not shiny
3 – 4 = slightly shiny
5 – 6 = shiny
7 – 8 = very shiny
9 – 10 = highly shiny

Metal or alloy	Color	Malleability	Ductility	Luster
1. Tin solder				
2. Copper wire				

Questions and Conclusions

1. Why is the solder called an alloy and the copper wire is not?

_____

_____

2. What was the source of the energy for changing the state of the solder?

_____

_____

Laboratory Activity 1 (continued)

3. Why was solder chosen to join the two copper wires together and not something like clay or glue?

_____

_____

_____

4. What happened when you tried to make your first soldering joint?

_____

_____

_____

5. How was the solder different from the copper wire when the finished product was made?

_____

_____

_____

_____

6. Why don't electricians just use solder wire instead of copper wire to make electrical connections?

_____

_____

_____

_____

Strategy Check

_____ Can you observe and describe the properties of tin solder?

_____ Can you use solder to connect copper wires?

Investigating Polymers

LAB **2** Laboratory Activity

Polymers are very large molecules made of many identical units linked together in a chain. The individual units, called monomers, can be very simple or rather complex. A single molecule of a polymer can contain tens of thousands of monomers. The identity of the monomers, the way they are linked, and the length of the chains are some of the characteristics that determine what the polymer looks like and how it can be used. In some polymers, the monomers link together end to end, resembling a string of identical beads. Some monomers contain side chains, or branches, and resemble a very long string of large paper clips attached in a chain with chains of small paper clips hooked on in just the same way at just the same interval. In some polymers, the way the monomers link together causes the polymer molecule to bend and twist and sometimes form crosslinks in the long chains. Some polymers, such as polyethylene, contain just carbon and hydrogen with carbon forming the backbone of the molecules. Other polymers contain elements other than carbon and hydrogen. Nylon contains nitrogen, and polyvinyl chloride (PVC) contains chlorine. Some polymers, such as the polymer that is sold as toy putty, have a silicone backbone rather than a carbon backbone.

Every difference in molecular structure holds the possibility that the polymer can be used in a different way. As chain length increases, physical properties of the polymer change. Polymers made from longer chains are more ductile and are harder than polymers with shorter chains. Longer chain molecules are more viscous than shorter chain molecules. More crosslinking within a polymer molecule usually results in a more rigid substance.

Strategy

You will observe properties of different polymers.
You will describe some properties of various polymers.

Materials

variety of samples of polymers
newspaper
wax paper
small paper cups

epoxy cement
large toothpicks
*popsicle sticks
superglue

rubber cement
bathroom caulking
toy putty
*Alternate materials

Procedure

Part A—Observing Physical Properties

1. Spread at least two or three sheets of newspaper over the surface of your lab table to protect the tabletop. Place a small sheet of wax paper on top of the newspaper.
2. Be sure to wear gloves when handling any of the materials in this experiment. Examine the properties of at least six polymers. List the names of the materials selected under *Materials* in Table 1 in the Data and Observations section. For polymers like caulking that are in containers, use a toothpick to put a small sample on the wax paper.

Observe the color and odor of each. Record your observations in Table 1 in the Data and Observations section. Note how thick the substances are (the thicker the substance, the higher the viscosity) and record your observation under *Viscosity* in Table 1. Observe how hard or brittle the solids are. Record your observations in Table 1.

3. Put the wax paper with the samples aside.

Laboratory Activity 2 (continued)

Part B—Comparing Physical Properties

1. Cover the newspaper with another sheet of wax paper.

2. Be sure to wear gloves when handling any of the materials in this experiment. Following the instructions your teacher gives, mix a small amount of epoxy glue in a small paper cup. Use a toothpick to stir the epoxy. Avoid getting any epoxy glue on your hands. Pour some of the mixed epoxy on the wax paper. Use a toothpick to spread the epoxy into a thin sheet.

3. Using separate toothpicks, spread small amounts of the superglue, the toy putty, the rubber cement, and the bathroom caulking into thin sheets at various places on the wax paper. You may have to apply a second, and perhaps a third, coat of rubber cement. Observe these samples for color and odor. Using a toothpick, observe the viscosity, and brittleness or hardness of the samples. Do not touch the samples with your fingers. Record your observations in Table 2.

4. Allow about 10 minutes for the polymers to dry. Test the slower drying polymers for dryness by poking them with a toothpick to see if any tackiness, or stickiness, remains. Wait to make your observations until the samples are dry.

5. When your samples are dry, once again observe them for color, odor, viscosity, brittleness, and hardness. Record your observations in Table 3 in the Data and Observations section.

6. Remove the thin sheets of dried polymers from the wax paper. Under *Adhesion* in Table 3, note whether the polymer came off the wax paper easily.

Data and Observations

Table 1

Material	Color	Odor	Viscosity/Brittleness/Hardness

Laboratory Activity 2 (continued)

Table 2

Initial Observations			
Material	**Color**	**Odor**	**Viscosity/Brittleness/Hardness**

Table 3

Final Observations				
Material	**Color**	**Odor**	**Viscosity/ Brittleness/ Hardness**	**Adhesion**

Questions and Conclusions

1. Describe the range of physical properties, including color, odor, viscosity, brittleness, and hardness in the six samples you selected in Part A.

_____

_____

_____

_____

_____

Laboratory Activity 2 (continued)

2. Describe some of the uses that the polymer samples have.

_____

_____

_____

3. Was the rubber cement or the epoxy glue harder when it dried? Which would you expect or to have more crosslinks in its molecules? Explain your answer.

_____

_____

_____

4. Would you expect the molecules that form a plastic bag to have longer or shorter chains than the molecules that form a milk carton? Explain your answer.

_____

_____

_____

Strategy Check

_____ Can you observe the properties of different polymers?

_____ Can you describe some properties of various polymers?

ANSWER KEY

Chapter 1

Laboratory Activity 1 (page 1)

Note: Remind students that all reflected waves–including sound, light, and water–obey the law of reflection.
Nondistorting, shatterproof safety mirrors can be used in place of traditional glass mirrors.

Data and Observations

Table 1

Data will vary.

1. Accept all reasonable answers.

2. **Sample data**

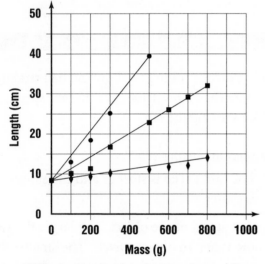

Width of rubber band: ● 2 mm ■ 4 mm ◆ 7 mm

Questions and Conclusions

1. The graphs describe how much each rubber band stretches as the mass that is causing it to stretch increases.

2. It measures the "stretchiness" or flexibility of the rubber band.

3. The steepness decreases as the widths of the rubber bands increase.

4. The flexibility of a rubber band decreases as its width increases.

5. Read the length that was measured for a mass of 0 g. A mass of 0 g means that nothing was hanging from the rubber band and the rubber band was unstretched.

6. Answers will vary.

7. Suspend the object from the rubber band and measure the length of the stretched rubber band. Use Graph 1 to determine the mass of the object from the length of the stretched rubber band.

Laboratory Activity 2 (page 5)

Note: Some students may recognize a connection between convex lenses and the curve called a "parabola" that is studied in mathematics.

Data and Observations

Table 1

Data will vary, depending on coins used.

Graph 1—Sample data

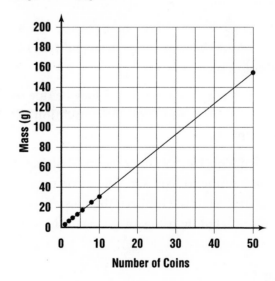

ANSWER KEY

Graph 2—Sample data

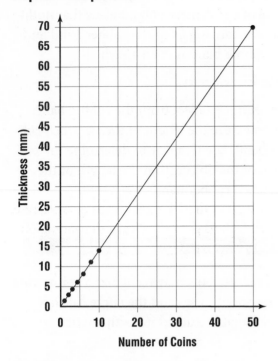

Questions and Conclusions

1. Each graph should be a straight line.

2. Answers will vary.

3. Answers will vary.

4. Answers will vary. Differences may be due to accuracy of the measurements, condition of the coins, etc.

5. Answers will vary. Differences may be due to accuracy of the measurements, condition of the coins, etc.

6. Yes. Students can multiply the mass of 1 coin by the number of coins to determine the mass of the coins. However, the masses will be more accurate using an average value.

Chapter 2

Laboratory Activity 1 (page 9)

Notes: Be sure that the pulling force being applied to the roller skater is constant. Students on roller skates should wear helmets and pads.

Questions and Conclusions

1. Answers will vary, but should demonstrate an understanding that constant force results in a constant acceleration.

2. The rate of acceleration remained constant.

3. Acceleration decreases as mass increases.

4. As the force increases, acceleration increases.

5. No movement would indicate that the skater's inertia was too great, and a force greater than 4-N would be required to move the skater.

6. Student answers will vary, but the notion should be rejected.

Laboratory Activity 2 (page 13)

Note: Practice rolling the bowling ball straight down the hall a few times at different speeds before starting the lab.

Questions and Conclusions

1. The faster trial is steeper and the slower trial is flatter.

2. The speed of the object. The larger the slope, the faster an object travels. The smaller the slope, the slower the object.

3. The object has stopped.

4. A bowling ball dropped from a great height would fall at a constant rate of 9.8 m/s². The bowling ball in this lab negatively accelerated as it travelled.

5. Student answers will vary.

6. Student answers will vary.

7. Distance is how far an object moves. Displacement is the distance and direction of the object from the starting point.

ANSWER KEY

Chapter 3

Laboratory Activity 1 (page 17)

Note: Students sometimes think that the shape of their graph is also the shape of the projectile's path. Help students see that if you make a distance/time graph of one complete bounce of a ball, the graph would be the same basic shape as those in the lab. **Lab Notes:** Assign three students as timers for each toy rocket flight. Instruct them that the first student will be responsible for measuring the total time the rocket is in flight. The second student will be responsible for measuring the time required for the rocket to reach the highest point of its trajectory. The third student will be responsible for measuring the time required for the rocket to fall back to Earth from the highest point of its trajectory.

To eliminate prejudicing the measurements, you may wish to have the timers exchange roles after several flights.

Data and Observations

Data will vary, depending on the type of rocket used.

Questions and Conclusions

1. Answers will vary.

2. Answers will vary. Students should recognize that average time up and average time down were almost equal to each other for each of the two sets of launches.

3. The number of pumps was kept constant so that conditions remained the same for all launches in a set. By keeping the number constant during each set of launches, averages of the three time measurements could be calculated.

4. The 15 pumps produced greater air pressure inside the rocket. When the rocket was launched, the increased air pressure caused a greater vertical velocity.

Laboratory Activity 2 (page 21)

Data and Observations

Mass of cart will vary.
Observations of motion will vary, but students should recognize that the cart begins to accelerate. Data in tables and graph will vary, depending on the mass of the cart.

Questions and Conclusions

1. the force of the falling 100-g mass (its weight) pulling on the cart (the weight of the 100-g mass is about 1 newton)

2. The force had to be constant so no new variables were introduced. Conditions must be kept constant during an experiment.

3. $0 \text{ g} - \text{m/s}$

4. The momentum of the cart increases the longer the force acts on it.

5. The rotation gives the shot an initial momentum before the thrust. Because the shot has this momentum, the thrust will produce a greater final momentum than if the shot was thrown from at rest.

Chapter 4

Laboratory Activity 1 (page 25)

Note: Instruct students to make sure the string is stretched taut before they release the pendulum.

ANSWER KEY

Lab Note: The pendulum hanging at rest, considered by itself, has no kinetic or potential energy. In relation to Earth, there is potential energy due to gravity because that pendulum could fall. At the atomic level, there is potential and kinetic energy due to forces and motions among and within atoms.

Data and Observations

Hypothesis: Accept all reasonable hypotheses.
Step 3: The pendulum has no kinetic or potential energy with respect to the apparatus. It does have potential energy with respect to Earth.
Step 4: The pendulum now has potential energy, with respect to the apparatus.

Table 1

Student's data will vary. The longer strings should show fewer swings than the shorter strings.

Questions and Conclusions

1. When the pendulum is hanging straight down, it has no potential energy or kinetic energy with respect to the apparatus. It does have potential energy with respect to Earth.

2. The pendulum has potential energy when it is held at a right angle to the stand.

3. the force of gravity

4. The shorter string should produce more swings then the longer string. However, both sinkers should cause the pendulum to behave the same.

5. Use shorter strings to increase the number of swings in a time period.

6.

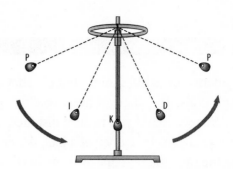

Laboratory Activity 2 (page 29)

Note: There are different grades of sandpaper. This will work best with one of the roughest grades.

Data and Observations

Height of ramp: Data will vary with the books chosen. The height should be expressed in centimeters. Types of surfaces: Accept any reasonable prediction.
Table: Students' data will vary. In general, soft, rough surface will reduce the kinetic energy more quickly than hard smooth surfaces will.

Questions and Conclusions

1. Soft, rough surfaces provided the greatest friction. The car traveled a shorter distance on these surfaces.

2. Smooth hard surfaces provided the least amount of friction.

3. The kinetic energy was changed into thermal energy due to friction.

4. Keeping the ramp the some in each trial makes everything associated with the ramp constant. This allows the distance traveled to be compared.

ANSWER KEY

5. To calculate the gravitational potential energy of the car at the top of the ramp, determine the mass of the car and the height of the ramp. Then use the formula.
GPE (J) = m (kg) × 9.8 m/s² = h (m)

6. Accept any reasonable prediction. The prediction should show an understanding of the role friction plays in transforming kinetic energy to thermal energy.

7. Students should understand that the smooth ice provides less friction than rough ice and that the hockey puck will travel farther on the smooth ice.

Chapter 5

Laboratory Activity 1 (page 33)

Note: Make sure some of the objects are very close in weight.
Lab Note: Use weights that can be added in multiples to balance the mobiles easily.

Data and Observations

Data will vary. For Table 1, weights depend on objects used. For Table 2, data will depend on the design of the mobile. For each balanced lever, the product of the resistance force and the resistance arm should be about equal to the product of the effort force and the effort arm.

Questions and Conclusions

1. No. The product of the distance and weight of the left side (250 N cm) does not equal the product of the right side (180 N cm).

2. For practical purposes, it has no effect. The weight of the string is negligible.

3. When the mass of the object being weighed equals the sum of the gram masses on the balance, the balance acts as a balanced lever.

4. a = 6N; b = 5N

Laboratory Activity 2 (page 37)

Lab Note: Remind students to convert the distance measurements from centimeters to meters.

Data and Observations

Table 1: Data will vary
Table 2: Data will vary
Table 3: Calculations will vary.
Table 4: Calculations will vary.
Graph 1: Data will vary
Graph 1: Data will vary

Questions and Conclusions

1. The effort distance is vary much greater using the block and tackle.

2. The effort force is very much less than the resistance force in the block and tackle.

3. In neither machine is the work output greater than the work input.

4. The single fixed pulley changes the direction of motion so, as the rope is pulled down, the flag raises.

5. The block and tackle multiplies the effort so an effort force less than the weight of the engine is needed to lift the engine.

6. Because there are more moving parts in a block and tackle, some of the work input is transferred into heat by friction. Likewise, in a block and tackle, some work input is done in raising the lower pulley. The work done in raising the pulley is not useful work.

Chapter 6

Laboratory Activity 1 (page 43)

Note: Remind students that the test tube and its contents are extremely hot. They should avoid touching the test tube or the piece of metal.

Lab Note: Prepare approximately 20-g samples of aluminum (X), copper (Y), and iron (Z). Prepare a boiling water bath. Using a ring stand and clamp, suspend a thermometer so that its bulb is submerged. Position the thermometer so that students can read the temperature of the water safely.

Data and Observations

Data will depend on sample.

Table 1

Data will depend on sample.

Questions and Conclusions

1. Answers will vary. Students' values should reflect those in Table 2.

2. The amount of energy that was gained by the water was equal to that lost by the hot metal. Because the specific heat of water is greater than that of the metal, the amount of heat transferred caused less of a change in the temperature of the water than it did in the temperature of the metal.

3. Both were probably at the same temperature because the water had a long period of time to transfer the heat from the hot plate to the metal and raise its temperature.

4. No. Because metals are good conductors of heat, the metal cans and aluminum foil would transfer heat quickly to the air. The heat gained by the water would not be an accurate measurement of the amount of heat lost by the piece of metal.

Laboratory Activity 2 (page 47)

Lab Note: Reminder—some children are highly allergic to nuts, especially peanuts. If you have a student who is allergic, substitute raisins or another energy food.

Lab Note: Use different nuts, such as peanuts, almonds, and walnuts, for food samples. Students can compare energy released by each type of food.

Lab Note: This activity actually measures the energy absorbed by the water from the burning food sample. Some energy will be absorbed by the flask and surrounding air.

Lab Note: Times of more than 2 minutes may be needed for some food samples.

Data and Observations

Data will depend on samples used.

Lab Note: Determine an average value for each food sample. Enter this value in the class data table.

Questions and Conclusions

1. the mass of substance burned, the mass of water heated, the change in temperature of the water, and the specific heat of water

2. The water temperature rises.

3. the energy gained by the water

4. Energy was absorbed by the flask and the surrounding air.

5. Answers will vary.

6. 209 J/0.4kg = Q/20.0 g Q = 10,450 J

Chapter 7

Laboratory Activity 1 (page 51)

Note: Remind students to wear gloves, goggles, and aprons at all times while handling the HCl as this solution could irritate or burn the skin.

ANSWER KEY

Data and Observations

Table 1

zinc, iron—bubbles form on surfaces of electrodes, 0.33

zinc, tin—bubbles form on surfaces of electrodes, 0.63

Questions and Conclusions

1. Bubbles were observed, indicating that gases were formed. The needle of the voltmeter moved, indicating that a current was produced.

2. the zinc and tin electrodes

3. No. Removing an alligator clip would break the path that the electrons follow. The electrons would stop flowing and there would be no current.

4. Current is a measure of the number of electrons moving. Voltage is a measure of the push that causes electrons to flow.

Laboratory Activity 2 (page 53)

Lab Note: A sheet of plastic foam may be used. If necessary, strip away about 0.5 cm of the insulation from the end of each of the lead wires of the battery clip.

Data and Observations

Part A

Step 8: The LED glows.

Step 9: the LED stops glowing.

Step 10: Both LEDs glow with equal brighness. LED 1 is less bright than in Step 8.

Step 11: Answers will vary. Accept all reasonable responses.

Step 12: LED 2 stopped glowing

Part B

Step 3: Both glow with equal brightness.

Step 4: Answers will vary. Accept all reasonable responses.

Step 5: LED 2 remains glowing with no change in brightness.

Step 6: The brightness did not change.

Step 7: Answers will vary. Accept all reasonable responses.

Step 8: LED 1 remains glowing with no change in brightness.

Questions and Conclusions

1. The 500-Ω resistor limits the current in the circuit so the LED won't "burn out."

2. No current flowed in the circuit.

3. The amount of current in the circuit decreased.

4. There was no change to the current flowing through the other LED.

5. The amount of current didn't change.

6. Because the current in each of the two LEDs was the same, the value of the current elsewhere, such as in the resistor, had to be double this value.

7. Answers will vary. Students should recognize that when two or more lamps are plugged into the wall outlet and one or the other is turned on or off, the other is not affected. They have the same characteristics as the LEDs that were in a parallel circuit.

Chapter 8

Laboratory Activity 1 (page 57)

Note: You can use waxed paper for the sheet of clear plastic. It will be easy to make into a funnel to return the iron filings to the container.

ANSWER KEY

Data and Observations

Figure 3

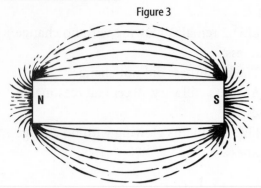

Figure 4

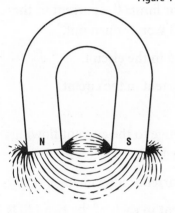

Figure 5

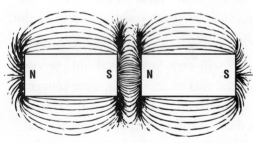

Figure 6

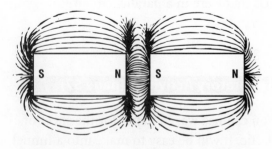

Figure 7

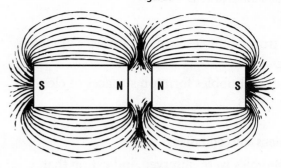

Figure 8

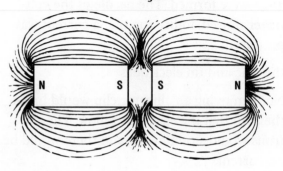

Questions and Conclusions

1. The iron filings are magnetic and align themselves along the magnetic field of the magnet.

2. Answers will vary with the strength of the two magnets used. The magnet that has the greater concentration of iron filings around it has greater strength.

3. The magnetic field is concentrated between the two unlike poles.

4. The magnetic field spreads away from the area between the two poles.

Laboratory Activity 2 (page 61)

Lab Note: The iron BBs can be purchased as #8 shot. Students should place the materials on sheets of newspaper or paper towels to catch spilled BBs.

ANSWER KEY

Data and Observations

Bolts alone: The bolts pick up no BBs. Therefore, they show no magnetic properties. Table: Data will vary. The number of BBs that the bolts pick up will increase with the number of turns of wire. **Lab Note:** Students should realize that the number of turns of wire is the independent variable and number of BBs picked up is the dependent variable. Accordingly, they should label the *x*-axis *Number of turns* and the *y*-axis *Number of BBs picked up.*

Questions and Conclusions

1. The force exerted by an electromagnet lifting an object is at least equal to the weight of the object being lifted. Because the weight of the BBs is directly related to the number of BBs, the number of BBs lifted is a measure of the strength of the magnetic force of the electromagnet.

2. The strength of the magnetic force increases as the number of turns of wire increases.

3. The graph is a straight line with a positive slope, indicating that the strength of the magnetic force increases as the number of turns of wire in an electromagnet increases.

4. Answers will vary but should be extrapolated from the students' data interpreted on the graph.

5. The bolts are experimental controls. To avoid any effect due to differences in the types of bolts or their sizes or shapes, the bolts, must be identical.

6. Each coil exerts a magnetic force independent of the other coils. The resulting force of more than one coil is equal to the sum of forces exerted by each coil.

Chapter 9

Laboratory Activity 1 (page 65)

Data and Observations
Graph 1

Students should realize that the power rating of the lightbulbs is the independent variable and the power output of the solar cell is the dependent variable. Accordingly, they should label the *x*-axis *Power rating of lightbulb* (W) and the *y*-axis *Power output of solar cell* (W).

Questions and Conclusions

1. the 100-W lightbulb

2. The power output of the solar cell is directly related to the power rating of the lightbulbs.

3. Answers will vary. The sunlight has the same effect as a 110-W lightbulb.

4. 1667 solar cells are needed.
   Students should use a ratio.
   x/1 solar cell = 100 W/0.060 W

Laboratory Activity 2 (page 69)

Lab Note: This activity might require two class periods.
Lab Note: You might wish to have the students build their solar water heaters (Part A) during one period and test the water heaters (Part B) on another day.
Lab Note: You might wish to have selected students assemble the solar water heaters as an out-of-class activity.
Lab Note: A heat lamp may be used on a cloudy day.
Lab Note: Demonstrate how to start a siphon. With the siphon bucket above the *OUT* tube, carefully suck on the *OUT* tube drawing water from the bucket, through the *IN* tube, into the system, and out the *OUT* tube.

ANSWER KEY

Data and Observations

Table 1

Data will vary. However, the temperature of the water should rise continuously.

Graph 1

Students should realize that time is the independent variable and temperature is the dependent variable. Accordingly, they should label the *x*-axis *Time* (*min*) and the *y*-axis *Temperature* (*°C*).

Questions and Conclusions

1. The temperature of the water slowly increases.

2. The shape of the graph indicates that the longer the water in the solar water heater was exposed to the Sun's energy, the warmer the water became.

3. Black materials absorb more radiant energy than light-colored materials.

4. Answers might include the following benefits: solar energy is renewable, costless, non-polluting, and efficient. Answers might include the following problems: solar energy is not available on cloudy days or at night, and installation of solar heating equipment is costly.

Chapter 10

Laboratory Activity 1 (page 73)

Notes: Wavelength is often measured from crest to crest. You could mention to students that wavelength can be found using any point on the wave, not just the crest.
Lab Note: Students may find it difficult to get satisfactory photos. You may wish to forego the photography and simply have the students sketch the waves.

Lab Note: In Part A, step 4 you may wish to increase the time to 60 seconds. Remind students that a yarn marker moves from a crest to a trough to a crest as one wave passes that point.
Lab Note: In Part B, step 2, It is important that students maintain the same frequency during each 30-second period.

Data and Observations

Data will depend on such factors as the type of rope used, its diameter, and its tautness.

Questions and Conclusions

1. The frequency of the waves increased.

2. The wavelength decreased.

3. The velocity remained constant.

4. The data indicate that the velocity of a wave moving through a material is independent of its frequency. The velocity of the wave remained constant even though its frequency increased.

Lab Note: Because taking a good photo of wave patterns is difficult, you may wish to have students attach their sketches of the patterns instead of photos.

Laboratory Activity 2 (page 77)

Data and Observations

1. circular

2. yes

3. straight line

4. The pulse reflects off of the barrier.

5. back towards the source

6. straight line

7. The wave bounces back.

8. a point on the other side of the paraffin block

ANSWER KEY

9. The wave that hits the block is reflected.

10. The wave that does not hit the block continues on in the same direction.

11. The waves speed up as they pass from deep to shallow water.

12. The waves that pass over the glass are curved.

13. The waves that do not pass over the glass are straight.

14. The waves that pass over the glass are faster than the waves that do not pass over the glass.

Questions and Conclusions

1. circular

2. reflects

3. Each part of the wave hits the barrier in succession, so they reflect in succession and maintain their circular shape

4. They move faster.

Chapter 11

Laboratory Activity 1 (page 81)

Note: Before beginning the lab, you could use a guitar to demonstrate and then discuss differences in pitch.
Lab Note: You may demonstrate the variations in pitch in a similar way with a guitar or violin.

Data and Observations

1. Answers will vary.

2. Thicker rubber bands produce lower-pitched sounds.

3. As the length of the rubber band is shortened, the pitch becomes higher; as the length increases, the pitch becomes lower.

Questions and Conclusions

1. The pitch of the sound rises as the length increases.

2. The frequency rises as the thickness decreases.

3. The longer the string the deeper the sound.

Laboratory Activity 2 (page 83)

Note: Remind students to use caution when working with the wire cutters, staples, hammer and nails.
For safety reasons, you could cut all the wire pieces beforehand. You could also use a staple gun to secure the wire coat hanger pieces to the wooden block. Freezer bags and plastic shopping bags could be used instead of plastic trash bags.
Lab Note: You might want to have each group perform for the class using the instruments they have made.

Data and Observations
Answers will vary

Questions and Conclusions

1. Twanger, xylophone, guitar, chimes

2. In a twanger, different lengths of wire produced different pitches. In the xylophone, different amounts of water in the beakers produced different pitches. In the guitar, different pitches were produced by rubber bands of different thicknesses and tightness. In the nail chimes, different sizes of nails produced different pitches.

3. The guitar is a stringed instrument. The twanger, xylophone, nail chimes, shakers, and drums all are percussion instruments.

ANSWER KEY

4. Since longer length produces lower frequency the number of waves passing a point decreases. With shorter lengths producing higher frequency, the number of waves passing a point increases.

Chapter 12
Laboratory Activity 1 (page 87)

Note: Students may need help with scientific notation. Remind them to move the decimal point to the left when multiplying by a number with a negative exponent.

Data and Observations

1. (1×10^{-6}) $(109) = 1 \times 103$; 1,000 nm; 1,000 mm

2. (7.5×10^{-7}) $(109) = 7.5 \times 102$; 750 nm; 750 mm

3. (6.25×10^{-7}) $(109) = 6.25 \times 102$; 625 nm; 625 mm

4. (5.75×10^{-7}) $(109) = 5.75 \times 102$; 575 nm; 575 mm

5. (5.25×10^{-7}) $(109) = 5.25 \times 102$; 525 nm; 525 mm

6. (4.5×10^{-7}) $(109) = 4.5 \times 102$; 450 nm; 400 mm

7. (4×10^{-7}) $(109) = 4 \times 102$; 400 nm; 400 mm

8. (3×10^{-8}) $(109) = 3 \times 10$; 30 nm; 30 mm

Questions and Conclusions

1. red, orange, yellow, green, blue, indigo, violet

2. Nanometers are too small to work with and anything larger than millimeters would be too large.

3. 2×10^{-2} m

4. 3×10^9 mm

5. The range of the wavelengths is so large that no scale would make the whole spectrum manageable.

Laboratory Activity 2 (page 91)

Note: Remind students to keep the burning candle a safe distance from the pickup coil. Students may think that only electrical devices can emit electromagnetic waves. Remind them that anything that has a changing electrical field, like a magnet, will also emit electromagnetic waves. A cordless phone is another common appliance that could be used.

Questions and Conclusions

1. Waves are produced by something that vibrates and carry energy from one place to another. Sound waves move through air because energy is transferred from particle to particle.

2. If the items produce the same frequency, the sound should be the same. If there are different frequencies, you should get destructive interference.

3. Anything that has a changing electrical field will emit electromagnetic waves because Earth's magnetic field provides the magnetic portion of the electromagnetic wave.

4. Anything that has a changing electrical field will produce electromagnetic waves.

5. Student answers will vary, but many will indicate that getting rid of electromagnetic waves will be impossible, as many of them are naturally occurring. Other students might indicate that we would have to revert to primitive means in order to get rid of all electromagnetic waves.

ANSWER KEY

Chapter 13

Laboratory Activity 1 (page 95)

Notes: You could point out to students that a prism actually refracts light twice–once when it enters the prism and once when it leaves the prism.

Lab Notes: Demonstrate focusing the prism's image by changing the orientation of the prism with respect to the light source and screen (white paper). Note that indigo may be difficult to distinguish in the spectrum.

Data and Observations
Part A

1. **a.** red

   b. orange

   c. yellow

   d. green

   e. blue

   f. violet

Part B

1. Repeating bands of color appear on the film.

2. Student drawings will vary.

Questions and Conclusions

1. When light travels from one material to another, its speed changes. If the light strikes the material at an angle, its direction changes. The change of speed is called refraction. Light waves of different wavelengths differ in the amount of refraction they undergo.

2. Destructive interference occurs when the crest of one wave arrives with the trough of another wave. The two waves cancel each other, and no color is produced. Constructive interference occurs when two

waves are in phase. The two waves produce a band of color that depends on their wavelengths.

3.

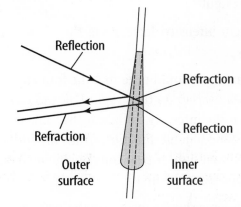

4. A spectrum produced by reflection is made from light that passes through a prism. The spectrum produced by a thin film is produced by the interference of light reflected from the two surfaces of the thin film.

5. **a.** refraction

   b. reflection

   c. interference

Laboratory Activity 2 (page 99)

Lab Notes: Photo resistors are available from scientific equipment and supply houses and electronics stores.

Data and Observations

1. Student answers will vary.

2. Student answers will vary.

Table 1
Students' data will vary.

Graph 1
Students' graph will vary.

ANSWER KEY

Questions and Conclusions

1. The graph indicates that the resistance of the photo resistor decreases with distance from the light.

2. Light intensity decreases as the distance from its source increases.

3. Students should note that the four steps of data overlap on the graph. This indicates that the intensity of light is the same at equal distances in all directions from the source and that light travels out equally in all directions from a source.

4. Students should recognize that the light from other sources will affect the photo resistor. With the room darkened, the photo resistor will respond to only the light from the light bulb.

5. Accept all reasonable answers.

6. If Earth were farther from the Sun, the intensity from the Sun's energy striking Earth would be less and its surface would be cooler. If the Sun were closer, the intensity of the solar energy striking Earth would be greater and its surface would be warmer.

Chapter 14

Laboratory Activity 1 (page 103)

Notes: Remind students that all reflected waves–including sound, light, and water–obey the law of reflection. Nondistorting, shatterproof safety mirrors may be used in place of traditional glass mirrors.
Lab Note: Have students use combs with long, wide teeth for best results.

Data and Observations

Observation of light rays in step 2 of the procedure: The light appears to travel in straight lines between the teeth of the comb.

Hypothesis: Answers will vary. Most students will state that there is an equality between the angles formed by the mirror and the incident and reflected rays or an equality between the angles of incidence and reflection as defined in the introduction.

Table 1
Data depend on angles used.

Questions and Conclusions

1. Because the bright areas behind the comb are straight and parallel, the light rays passing between the teeth that form these areas must be traveling in straight and parallel lines.

2. Almost all the light is reflected from the shiny coating on the back of the mirror, not the glass surface on the front of the mirror.

3. The angle of reflection increased.

4. The angle of incidence equals the angle of reflection for any reflected light ray.

Student tracings will vary.

Laboratory Activity 2 (page 107)

Note: Some students may recognize a connection between convex lenses and parabolas that are studied in mathematics.

Data and Observations
Table 1
Data will vary.

Table 2
Data will vary.

Questions and Conclusions

1. The image appears larger than the object and is erect.

2. Answers will vary. Students should recognize that the image appears to be located behind the screen. However, no light that could form the image can come from behind the opaque screen. Therefore, the image is a virtual image.

3. Answers will vary.

4. The magnifying power of a lens increases as its curvature increases. The magnifying power of a lens is equal to focal length divided by 25 cm minus the focal length of the lens.

5. Yes. The semiround shape of the water drop acts as a convex lens that can form enlarged, erect, virtual images.

6. Area of image = 2 cm × 4 cm = 8 cm²

Chapter 15

Laboratory Activity 1 (page 111)

Notes: Ethanol is flammable, so make sure there are no open flames when students are working. Tell students to fill only one well of the microplate with the water/ethanol mixture. Students must avoid getting liquid in any of the other wells.

Students must not spill the mixture in the well of the microplate when they insert the microplate into the bag.

If students have difficulty recognizing the different dyes, try the procedure again with a larger ink spot or even a line of ink. Also, letting the filter paper dry overnight may make the dyes more visible.

Lab Note: In Procedure step 3, students must draw the lines with pencils, not pens.

Data and Obesrvations

Answers will vary. Students should indicate that various dyes have separated from the inks and moved different distances along the strip filter paper.

Table 1—observations will vary depending on the type of ink in each marking pen.

Questions and Conclusions

1. Answers will vary. Because each ink left a different pattern of colors on the strip of filter paper, students might suggest that the pattern was written in color.

2. A physical change took place, because the dyes separated according tot each dye's ability to dissolve in ethanol, which is a physical property.

3. There would be no separation of colors on the strip of filter paper.

4. Answers will vary. In general, blue dyes will travel the shortest distances.

5. She will see only one color on each strip. The solution she used to spot the strip contained only one dye because she made the solution by dissolving a single component dye and not a mixture of dyes.

Laboratory Activity 2 (page 115)

Notes: In Part A, remind students that the bottle that appears empty actually contains the same matter as the air around it.

Have students test their circuits with the light-bulb and battery before testing the different materials.

Students must use caution when using hydrochloric acid as it can cause severe burns. Use weak solutions.

Have students move the burning match slowly toward the test tube to avoid a flare-up when the flame comes in contact with oxygen from the reaction.

Suggest that students add drops of iodine to several parts of the toast and compare the results.

ANSWER KEY

Lab Note: You may wish to use two class periods for this experiment. Prior to class time, prepare a bottle or flask containing sand (solid), water (liquid), and air (gas). Stopper the bottle.

Data and Observations

States of matter in the bottle: sand (solid), water (liquid), and air and water vapor (gas). Some students may not identify air or water vapor, since they are invisible.

Table 1

iron—dark silver; varies; solid; metallic, heavy
wood—tan-brown; varies; solid; soft, fibrous
rubber—varies; varies; solid; pliable
copper—orange; varies; solid; soft, metallic

Table 2

iron—yes; yes
wood—no; no
rubber—no; no
copper—no; yes

Table 3

chalk, hydrochloric acid—gas bubbles produced, extinguishing the flame
iodine, toasted bread—red color of iodine is unchanged
iodine, untoasted bread—red iodine turns blue-black

Questions and Conclusions

1. A solid (sand) and a liquid (water) were visible. Gases (air and water vapor) were present, but not visible.

2. Both are solids at room temperature, metals, and conductors

3. The observations do not involve a change in chemical composition. Physical properties describe the nature of matter.

4. A chemical change took place. A gas (CO_2) was produced.

5. The gas is odorless and colorless. The gas is produced when chalk ($CaCO_3$) and hydrochloric acid react. The gas does not promote combustion.

6. A chemical change took place. The red iodine solution reacted with the starch in the bread and changed it to blue-black. (Iodine is used as a chemical indicator of starch)

Chapter 16

Laboratory Activity 1 (page 119)

Notes: Make sure there are no open flames when students are working with ethanol—it is flammable.
Make sure that students do not taste the corn syrup. Tasting substances, even edible ones, is not good laboratory practice.
As students squeeze the air out of their pipettes, tell them not to release the bulb because it will suck air back into it.

Questions and Conclusions

1. corn oil, ethanol, water, corn syrup

2. The densities of corn oil and ethanol are less than that of water. Corn syrup is denser than water.

3. The corn oil would rise to the top and float on the surface of the water. Because corn oil is less dense than water and less dense materials float on more dense materials, the corn oil will float on water.

4. ethanol—0.80, corn oil—0.65, corn syrup—1.40

5. Because it is a ratio of measurements that have the same units, the units cancel out.

ANSWER KEY

Notes: Have students wear gloves when using heat to seal the end of their pipettes. Students must avoid touching the end of the pipette until it has had plenty of time to cool.

If the pipettes begin to leak when placing books on them, tell students that they need to repeat Part A with a new pipette.

In Part B, students must make sure the end of the pipette stays in the solution during the entire procedure.

Data and Observations

Part A—Volume and Pressure of a Gas

Answers will vary.

Table 1

Data will vary.

Part B—Volume and Temperature of a Gas

Answers will vary.

Table 2

Data will vary.

Lab Note: You might wish to have students verify that Graph 1 illustrates an inverse relationship. If two variables are inversely related, the product of the two variables at any point on the graph is a constant. Thus, $y_1 \times 1 = y_2 \times 2$. For example, using the numerical values from the second and fourth data points, $48 \times 2 = 24 \times 4$. Because the two products are equal, the graph illustrates that the volume and pressure of gas are inversely related.

Graph 1

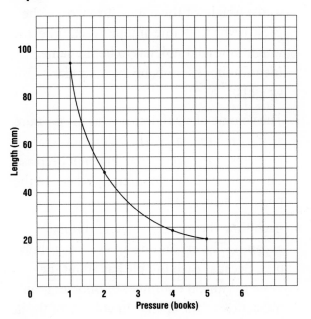

Graph 2

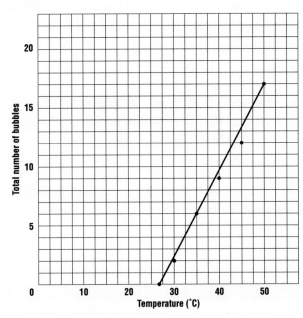

Questions and Conclusions

1. The air trapped in the stem of the pipette forms a cylinder. The volume of a cylinder is equal to the area of the base times its length. Because the area of the base of the air column does not change, the volume of the trapped air is directly related to the length of the air column.

2. The pressure on the bulb is directly related to the weight of the books. To increase the pressure by the same amount each time, the weight of each book has to be the same. Identical books probably have similar weights.

3. The volume of a gas decreases as the pressure acting on it increases. The volume of a gas increases as the pressure acting on it decreases. The volume of a gas is inversely related to the pressure acting on it.

4. Each time the air is heated, its volume expands. The expanding air escapes as bubbles. Because each bubble has about the same volume, the number of bubbles is an indication of the change in volume of the air as it is heated. The total number of bubbles indicates the volume that the air has expanded since its temperature has been raised from room temperature.

5. Answers will vary.

6. The same number of bubbles being released indicates that the volume of the gas changed the same amount every time its temperature was raised 5°C.

7. The volume of a gas varies directly with its temperature.

Chapter 17

Laboratory Activity 1 (page 129)

Notes: In addition to aprons and goggles, students should wear gloves when handling chemicals. Suggest students observe each substance in the wells of the microplate before they add the metal strips.

Remind students that they are looking for color changes and precipitates (granules) in each solution.

Lab Note: Students will require $0.1M$ (mole) of each of the aqueous solutions.
Lab Note: 10 mm lengths of wire of each of the metals may be used.

Data and Observations

Observations will vary.

Table 1

Data will vary.

Questions and Conclusions

1. These wells were controls with which to compare the color of the solutions in the wells to which metals had been added.

2. These wells were controls with which to compare the color of the metal strips in the wells to which solutions had been added.

3. The metal strips were cleaned to remove any dirt or materials that may have prevented a chemical reaction from taking place.

4. Mg, Al, Zn, Ni, Fe, Pb, Cu

Laboratory Activity 2 (page 133)

Notes: Give students shallow plastic food containers with fairly large surface areas so the pennies are not stacked on top of each other. Make sure students understand that the theoretical probability of a penny landing on heads or tails is 1:2 or $\frac{1}{2}$.

Data and Observations

Students may need to add row(s) to the table if they still have pennies left in the box after the seventh shaking.

Questions and Conclusions

1. The shaking process represented the process of radioactive decay.

ANSWER KEY

2. The heads-up side represented the unstable isotope. The tails-up side represented the stable atom.

3. The half was the shaking time, 20 seconds, that it took for approximately half the pennies to turn from heads-up to tails-up.

4. The total number of atoms (100) does not change, but the number of stable and unstable atoms does change.

5. With more trials, the results come closer to the expected results of half heads and half tails after each 20-second shaking.

6. There should be 6 or 7 heads-up pennies after four shakes of the box, or 80 seconds of decay.

7. After 60 seconds, or three shakes of the box, 224 pennies would be stable.

Chapter 18

Laboratory Activity 1 (page 137)

Note: You will need to plan several days ahead in order to have irradiated seeds on hand.
Lab Note: Samples of seeds that have been exposed to different levels of radiation may be ordered from many biological supply houses. If you prefer, request your dentist to irradiate the seeds using an X-ray machine. Place samples of the seeds in carefully labeled plastic sandwich bags and have your dentist expose the samples for different periods of time ranging from 0 to 20 seconds.

Data and Observations
Table 2

Observations will vary. Generally there will be less germination among the irradiated seeds than among the nonirradiated seeds.

Questions and Conclusions

1. These seeds are used as experimental controls with which to compare the seeds exposed to radiation.

2–7. Answers will vary depending on student data.

Laboratory Activity 2 (page 141)

Data and Observations

Step 7. Prediction of number of split peas removed: Answers will vary. Accept all reasonable responses.
Step 9. Prediction of number of observations until there are not split peas remaining: Answers will vary. Accept all reasonable responses.

Table 1
Data will vary.

Graph 1

Students should realize that time is the independent variable and the number of nuclei remaining is the dependent variable. Accordingly, students should label the x-axis *Time (min)* and the y-axis *Nuclei remaining*.

Questions and Conclusions

1. Answers will vary slightly. The half-life is about 5.1 minutes.

2. Answers will vary slightly. 56; 34

3. The split peas represent the nuclei of a radioactive element that could decay. However, the lima beans represent the nuclei of atoms that are not radioactive. These nuclei are stable and do not undergo natural radioactive decay.

4. Each nucleus of element A that decayed became a stable nucleus of element B. As the number of nuclei of element A decreased, the number of nuclei of element B increased.

5. Only the last question (c) can be answered. It is impossible to predict either which split pea or when a particular split pea will fall flat side up. However, because there are so many split peas being used, one can predict how many split peas should be remaining after 3 observations. (About 34 peas should be remaining after 3 half-lives.)

Chapter 19

Laboratory Activity 1 (page 145)

Notes: Prepare $HCl(aq)^3 M$ for the hydrochloric acid solution.

Students must wear gloves, goggles, and aprons at all times while handling the HCl and $Ca(OH)_2$, as either of these solutions could irritate or burn the skin.

Tell students to be careful when handling the pipette with the slit, as it could easily leak hydrochloric acid even when taped.

Make sure students do not extinguish the glowing ember before inserting the toothpick into the pipette containing CO_2.

Lab Note: Use HCl $(aq)^3$ M for hydrochloric acid. Use $CaCO_3(cr)$ for the marble chips. Use a saturated solution of $Ca(OH)_2(aq)$ for the lime water.

Data and Observations

Part A

Step 12: Answer will vary. Bubbles of a clear, colorless gas are produced.

Part B

Step 2: solution is clear and colorless.
Step 6: Solution has milky appearance.
Step 10: The glowing tip of the toothpick is quickly extinguished.

Questions and Conclusions

1. When carbon dioxide gas and lime water are mixed, the resulting solution containing calcium carbonate has a milky appearance. This reaction can be used to determine if a gas is carbon dioxide.

2. When the glowing tip of the toothpick is inserted in carbon dioxide gas, it is quickly extinguished because carbon dioxide gas does not support combustion. This test can be used to determine if a gas is carbon dioxide.

3. A soft drink is a solution of carbon dioxide and water. When a can of a soft drink is opened, the carbon dioxide gas comes out of the solution, forming bubbles. When hydrochloric acid and marble chips are mixed, a chemical reaction takes place and carbon dioxide gas, a new substance, is produced.

Laboratory Activity 2 (page 149)

Notes: Students should wear goggles, gloves, and aprons at all times while handling bleach and cobalt nitrate.

Bleach and cobalt nitrate should not be mixed or allowed to react other than in the controlled situation of the lab procedure.

Students should use care when squeezing the air out of the pipette filled with bleach in step 9. They could inadvertently squirt bleach if not careful.

To avoid flare-ups, have students light the ends of their toothpicks away from the oxygen-filled pipette. Also, make sure the flame of the burning toothpick is out–leaving only the glowing ember– before it is inserted into the oxygen-filled pipette.

Lab Note: Use $Co(NO_3)_2$ (aq) $0.1M$ for the cobalt nitrate solution. Household bleach is sodium hypochlorite, $NaOCl(aq)$.

ANSWER KEY

Data and Observations
Part A
Step 11: Answer will vary. Bubbles of a clear, colorless gas are produced.

Part B
Step 4: The toothpick burns rapidly.

Questions and Conclusions
1. Oxygen gas is needed for combustion. The oxygen allows the toothpick to continue to burn.

2. $O_2(g)$

3. Carbon dioxide and water

4. **a.** NaOCl: sodium (Na), oxygen (O), and chlorine (Cl); $Co(NO_3)_2$: cobalt (Co), nitrogen (N), and oxygen (O)

   b. NaOCl: 1; $Co(NO_3)_2$: 6

Chapter 20

Laboratory Activity 1 (page 153)

Notes: To avoid spills, consider dispensing the silver nitrate and sodium iodide yourself directly to students' microplates. Tell students to observe and record the properties of each solution before they add the solutions to the wells with hydrochloric acid. The solutions should be in clear test tubes.

Lab Note: Prepare samples (0.1M) of the six solutions used in Part A. Label the solution containers 1 through 6, in random order. Use these six solutions as the unknown solutions in Part B.

Data and Observations
Table 1
Observations may vary, but physical descriptions should be similar to those provided.

1. no reaction; no visible reaction; white solid, $PbCl_2(cr)$; white solid, $AgCl(cr)$; gas bubbles, Co_2 (g); no visible reaction

2. no visible reaction; no reaction; no visible reaction; no visible reaction; brown liquid, $Fe2(CO_3)$ (aq); no visible reaction

3. white solid, $AgCl(cr)$; no visible reaction; no visible reaction; no reaction; no visible reaction; yellow solid, $AgI(cr)$

4. gas bubbles, $CO_2(g)$; brown liquid, $Fe2(CO_3)_3(ag)$; white solid, $PbCO_3(cr)$; no visible reaction; no reaction; no visible reaction

5. no visible reaction; no visible reaction; yellow solid, $PbI_2(cr)$; yellow solid, $AgI(cr)$, no visible reaction; no reaction

Table 2
Data will depend on the sample used, but should closely resemble one set from Table 1.

Questions and Conclusions
1. Answers will depend on the sample solutions used, but the unknown sample should be identified as one of the solutions used in Part A.

2. Answers will depend on sample solution used but will probably include color and state.

3. The reaction products of the five known substances were observed and the physical characteristics were noted. The product of reaction of the sample solution with each of the five known solutions was then compared with the reaction products from the solutions. The known set that best matched the unknown was used to identify the sample solution.

4. No; there is no data or reaction products to use for comparison.

ANSWER KEY

Notes: The color code of 2000-Ω resistor is red-black-red. The fourth strip may be gold or silver or not there at all. Between tests have students use distilled water to rinse the ends of the wire. Tell students that tap water usually contains some ions and has some conductivity, so it is important to use distilled water when mixing solutions to test for conductivity. To avoid causing chemical reactions, students must not mix any solutions in this experiment. You may want to distribute the solutions yourself.

Lab Note: Prepare 0.1M solutions of the chemicals listed.

Lab Note: Strip 1 cm of insulation from each end of each 20-cm length of copper wire.

Data and Observations

Data will vary slightly. Solutions in wells 1 through 3 are good conductors (+), in well 4 is a fair conductor (−), and solutions in wells 5 through 7 have no conductivity.

Questions and Conclusions

1. The conductivity of distilled water is zero.

2. The conductivity of the distilled water was measured as a control to show that the measured conductivity is from the dissolved substance. Because the conductivity of water is zero, any conductivity demonstrated by a solution indicates that the dissolved substances in the solution caused the conductivity.

3. The solutions that do not conduct electricity contain ionic compounds.

4. Each solution that does not conduct electricity contains a compound that contains carbon, which forms covalent bonds.

5. Solutions of ionic compounds have good conductivity. Solutions of covalent compounds have no conductivity.

Chapter 21

Notes: Point out that the pipette is supposed to be inside the closed bag with the sodium hydrogen carbonate. If students' bags do not seal well, have them retry the experiment with another bag.

Lab Note: Add 0.3 g of solid sodium hydrogen carbonate to each sandwich bag.

Data and Observations

Data will vary.
Mass of bag before: 10.8 g
Observations from Step 6: Answers will vary. Students should observe bubbling, indicating that a gas or gases are begin produced.
Mass of bag after: 10.8 g
Students may see a slight decrease in the mass of the bag and its contents after the reaction. This is due to an increase in the buoyant force on the inflated bag.

Questions and Conclusions

1. The bag was sealed so that no matter could enter or leave the bag during the reaction.

2. Gas bubbles were formed and started to expand the plastic bag when the solid sodium hydrogen carbonate and hydrochloric acid solution were mixed.

3. Answers will vary. The students should recognize that the mass of the plastic bag and its contents before the reaction is equal to the mass of the plastic bag and its contents after the reaction.

4. Yes. Because the mass of the plastic bag and its contents as well as the masses of the plastic bag and the pipet themselves did not change during the reaction, the total mass of substances that reacted is the same as the total mass of substances that were formed.

ANSWER KEY

Laboratory Activity 2 (page 165)

Notes: Have students use small bunches of steel wool in Part A. The steel wool should be in a loose bunch for best results. Steel wool burns very hot and can spark, so students should be careful. The remaining steel wool and ash can remain hot for some time after it stops burning and should not be handled. This procedure also produces smoke, so adequate ventilation is needed.

The nail in Part C should not be rusty or galvanized (zinc coated). Steel wool could also be used in this experiment.

Data and Observations
Part A—Synthesis Reaction

1. Answers will vary.

2. silver-gray

3. dark gray-black

Part B—Decomposition Reaction

1. Answers will vary.

2. white solids and clear, colorless liquid

3. The flaming splint was extinguished.

Part C—Single Displacement Reaction
Answers will vary.

Table 1

1. silver; dark blue

2. red; light blue

Questions and Conclusions

1. iron; oxygen; iron (III) oxide

2. $O_2(g) + 2Fe(s) \rightarrow 2\,FeO(s)$

3. Sodium hydrogen carbonate (baking soda); carbon dioxide; sodium carbonate

4. $2NaHCO_3(s) \rightarrow CO_2(g) + Na_2CO_3(s) + H_2O(clear)$

5. Iron; copper (II) sulfate; Iron (II) sulfate; copper

6. $Fe(s) + CuSO_4(aq) \rightarrow FeSO_4(aq) + Cu(s)$

Chapter 22

Laboratory Activity 1 (page 169)

Notes: Have students wear gloves when handling and pouring hot water.

Make sure students do not shake the bottles of soda water before opening them.

At the beginning of the experiment, tell students to immediately add salt to the hot tap water.

For additional data, have students record the temperature of the hot and cold water. Suggest that students retry the experiment, varying the water temperature even further.

Data and Observations
Table 1

A—answers will vary; 1
B—answers will vary; 3
C—answers will vary; 5
D—answers will vary; 6
E—answers will vary; 2
F—answers will vary; 4

Part B

Bubbles of gas appeared in the opened bottle. No bubbles are seen in the unopened bottle.

Table 2

A—little or no bubbling
B—much bubbling
C—much bubbling

Questions and Conclusions

1. Many small particles dissolve faster than one large particle.

2. Salt dissolves in water faster at higher temperatures.

3. Stirring increases the speed at which salt dissolves.

4. The pressure in the soda water bottle was decreased by opening the bottle. When the bottle was opened, bubbles of CO_2 gas escaped from the soda water.

5. Heating, stirring, and reducing the pressure all increase the bubbling rate of soda water.

6. Shaking the bottle (similar to stirring) causes carbon dioxide to escape from the solution. This released carbon dioxide gas increases the pressure on the liquid inside the bottle. When the bottle is opened, there is a sudden reduction of the increased pressure. The dissolved gases quickly come out of solution and expand rapidly, forcing the soda out explosively.

Laboratory Activity 2 (page 173)

Notes: When measuring the water temperature, students should not let the thermometer touch the beaker itself.

The change in mass of the pie plates due to evaporation will be slight. Students will need to take careful measurements.

Have students record their observations of the pie plates after the liquid has evaporated.

Lab Note: Aluminum pot-pie pans are used as evaporating dishes.

Lab Note: Prepare 5-gram samples of NaCl and KNO_3 prior to class.

Lab Note: Point out that for water, 1 mL = 1g. Students should use the proportion mass of dissolved salt/mass of liquid evaporated = solubility/100.

Data and Observations

Students answers will vary.

Questions and Conclusions

1. Excess salt and impurities settled to the bottom of each test tube.

2. KBr

3. The solubility of each salt would increase.

4. **a.** The solubility of NaCl remains almost constant, rising only slightly with increasing temperature.

   b. The solubility of KBr will rise at an increasing rate with increasing temperature.

5. The two salts have equal solubilities at 49°C. Student answers will vary.

Chapter 23

Laboratory Activity 1 (page 177)

Note: The results of this lab will vary depending upon how well students mixed and diluted the solutions. Students must follow the directions carefully, rinsing the pipette with distilled water after each step in the procedure. Point out that each successive acid and base well is 10 times weaker than the previous one.

Data and Observations
Table 1
Wells:

1. red	7. green
2. red	8. green
3. orange	9. blue
4. yellow	10. blue
5. green	11. violet
6. green	12. violet

ANSWER KEY

Table 2

Data will vary. Samples: lemon juice, yellow/orange, 3–4; milk, green, 6–7; liquid soap, green, 9–10

Questions and Conclusions

1. Acids have pH values less than 7 and bases have pH values greater than 7.

2. acids—lemon juice, milk; base-liquid soap

3. 7, green

4. A universal indicator is a mixture of indicators that can be used to determine a wide range of pH values.

Laboratory Activity 2 (page 181)

Note: This lab approximates the effects of acid rain by dissolving carbon dioxide in water, forming carbonic acid. Acid rain in nature is not caused by carbon dioxide.

Data and Observations

Observations will vary.

Questions and Conclusions

1. carbon dioxide, CO_2 (g)

2. The gas represents acid rain.

3. The process is called diffusion.

4. The lengths of soda straws were placed in the four corners of the microplate to hold the plastic bag away from the microplate. This created an "atmosphere" in the bag.

5. Answers will vary. Students should recognize that the chemicals that cause acid rain enter the atmosphere as gases. Because the atmosphere is in constant motion, the gases can be carried great distances before they dissolve and fall to Earth as acid rain.

6. Answers will vary. Factors may include wind and geological structures such as mountains, valleys, and lakes.

Chapter 24

Laboratory Activity 1 (page 185)

Notes: Solutions X and Y will need to be prepared beforehand.

Remind students that there are two types of digestion–mechanical and chemical–at work. Students should wear gloves when handling the heated test tubes.

Lab Note: A solution containing diastase, an enzyme in saliva, will be used in this activity. Lugol's solution is normally yellow-brown in color and changes to blue-black in the presence of starch. Benedict's solution is normally blue in color and changes to yellow, then to red, in the presence of boiling glucose solution.

Lab Note: Solution X: 3g cornstarch/100 mL H_2O. Solution Y: 5 mL corn syrup/100 mL H_2O).
starch indicator solution: Lugol's solution.
sugar indicator solution: Benedict's solution.
saliva substitute: diastase of malt.

Lab Note: Prepare a boiling water bath for students to use in the experiment.

Part B, step 5: Benedict's solution will indicate glucose only if the sample is at 100°C. Lugol's solution shows a good color change with starch at 35°C–40°C

Data and Observations

Table 1—tube A: to blue-black, indicates starch; tube B: no color change, no indicator; tube C: no color change, no indicator; tube D: to yellow, then red, indicates sugar.
Table 2—5 mins: dark blue, blue; 10 mins: brownish, blue; 15 mins: yellow, yellow-red.

Questions and Conclusions

1. Answers will vary. Students should discuss how the blue-black color indicating starch in tube B fades over time. This indicates that the starch is being broken down. The saliva was breaking the starch down into sugars.

2. The water bath simulates body temperature. The breakdown of starch by saliva in the mouth normally occurs between 35[dg]C and 40[dg]C.

3. Answers will vary. Students should discuss how starch from the plain cracker is digested by saliva in the mouth. The starch breaks down into sugars, which provide the sweet taste.

4. No. The indicator solutions can be used only to detect sugar or starch. A deeper color does not necessarily indicate more sugar or starch. A deeper color could result from a high concentration of the indicator itself.

Laboratory Activity 2 (page 189)

Notes: The vitamin C indicator and solution should be prepared beforehand.

Explain to students the importance of rinsing the pipette after each use so that the solutions are not mixed.

Lab Note: Vitamin C indicator: indophenol testing reagent (lg/liter); Vitamin C solution: L-ascorbic acid, $C_6H_8O_6$(*cr*) (1g/liter)

	1	2	3	4	5	6
A	⊕	⊕	⊕	⊕	○	○
B	⊕	⊕	⊕	○	○	○
C	⊕	⊕	○	○	○	○
D	⊕	○	○	○	○	○

Questions and Conclusions

1. The concentration of the solutions in the wells decreases.

ANSWER KEY

2. The vitamin C solution had the greatest concentration of vitamin C. The indicator solution reacted with the contents of more of the wells containing vitamin C solutions than those containing the two orange juices and the orange drink.

3. Answers will vary. In most cases the freshly squeezed orange juice will have the greatest concentration of vitamin C.

4. 96 mL:mL/15 mL = 32 mg/5 mg

5. Experiments will vary. In one possible experiment, vitamin C indicator could be added to 5 different orange juice samples. The samples could be exposed to the air for 0, 15, 30, 45, and 60 minutes prior to adding the indicator.

Chapter 25

Laboratory Activity 1 (page 193)

Note: Mention that a soldering tool is very hot and that solder does not come out of it. You may want to require students to wear gloves when working near the soldering tool. You will need to cut the copper wire pieces beforehand.

Data and Observations
1. tin solder: gray, 5–6, 7–8, 3–4
2. copper wire: brown, 7–8, 9–10, 7–8

Students' data will vary. Students should be aware that solders and other alloys will conduct electricity at varying degrees. Also, once solder has been melted and used it becomes much more brittle and less ductile. However, its shininess increases.

Questions and Conclusions
1. The solder is made of tin, lead, and other compounds or elements. Copper is a pure metal.

2. The source of energy was the heat from the tip of the soldering gun.

3. Since the solder is a metal alloy it will conduct electricity. Clay or glue will not. A junction made by solder will permit electrical current to pass through it while the other materials will act as resistors or nonconductors.

4. At first the solder just seemed to burn up or go all over the place. We had to learn how to use just the correct amount of heat to make a successful joint without losing the solder.

5. The solder was more brittle than before. It had become less ductile and malleable. Its luster had increased, however.

6. As an alloy, the solder is not as strong as the copper wire. It is much more likely to break. If the heat were applied to it first, it would be too brittle to use.

Laboratory Activity 2 (page 197)

Note: Some of the substances have strong fumes associated with them. Be sure that students immediately seal them back up after each use. The room that you use should be well ventilated.
Lab Note: Provide students with a wide variety of polymers that they might encounter in their everyday life. Samples can include, but are not limited to, plastic bottles and bottle caps, plastic bags, clothing or fabrics (nylon, rayon, orlon, acrylic, polyester), zcarpet samples, vinyl flooring, vinyl siding, tires, food containers, plastic wrap, rubber, electrical insulation, bullet-proof vests, toys, ropes, fishing line, threads, latex or acrylic paint. Avoid including the materials used in Part B of this Laboratory Activity.
Lab Note: Some of the materials contain volatile compounds. Be sure the room you use is well ventilated.

ANSWER KEY

Part A

Lab Note: Note the directions on the label for the epoxy glue and pass these on to the students. **Lab Note:** The definition of *superglue* is a glue that becomes adhesive through polymerization rather than evaporation of a solvent.

Data and Observations

Table 1

Students' answers will vary with the polymers they selected to investigate.

Tables 2 and 3

Students' answers may vary with the brands of the polymers used. In general, epoxy cement and superglue are not viscous initially but dry very hard. Rubber cement and caulking are quite viscous and dry soft and with some degree of flexibility. Silly Putty is very viscous and does not change over 10 minutes.

Questions and Conclusions

1. Students' answers will vary with the variety of polymers selected.

2. Student answers will vary with the samples provided. The lists should include common uses but may also include some relatively unknown uses.

3. The epoxy glue, which is very hard when it has set, probably has a more crosslinking. More crosslinking generally results in a harder material.

4. Because hardness increases with chain length, the molecules in the milk carton probably have a longer chain length than those in the plastic bag.